Essential Maths 7 Core

Homework Book

Elmwood Education

First published 2019 by
Elmwood Education Limited
Unit 5 Mallow Park
Watchmead
Welwyn Garden City
AL7 1GX
Tel. 01707 333232

© Michael White
The moral rights of the authors have been asserted.
Database right Elmwood Education (maker)

ISBN 9781 906 622 763

Typeset and illustrated by Tech-Set Ltd., Gateshead, Tyne and Wear.

CONTENTS

UNIT 6

UNIT 1

1.1 Whole number arithmetic review

1 The digit 7 in the number 6718 stands for 7 hundreds or 700.
State the value of each digit underlined below:
   a 6<u>3</u>8   **b** <u>8</u>172   **c** 937<u>8</u>14   **d** <u>5</u>846832

2 Write these numbers in figures.
   a Forty-eight thousand and three
   b Seventeen thousand and twenty-four
   c Two and a half thousand

3 Using all the figures below once only, write down the smallest number possible and the largest number possible.
   a 4, 7, 1, 8   **b** 3, 6, 4, 9   **c** 5, 2, 8, 6, 9

4 Colin wins £8 104 653 on the National Lottery. Write this number in words.

5 Write down the numbers in order, from the smallest to the largest.
   a 3465   3219   3345   3280
   b 9148   9213   9018   9174   9306

6 Write these numbers in words.
   a 4315   **b** 70 000   **c** 32 140   **d** 6 842 300

7 **a** Which number is 100 more than 1649?
   b Which number is 1000 less than 2580?
   c Which answer in parts **a** and **b** is larger and by how much?

8 Copy and fill in the empty boxes.
   a $3 \times \square + 6 = 306$ **b** $5 \times \square + 3 = 5003$ **c** $4 \times \square + \square = 49$

   d $6 \times \square + 5 = 65$ **e** $2 \times \square + \square = 208$ **f** $9 \times \square + 4 \times \square = 9040$

9 Anjali has three quarters of a million pounds. She buys a house for £470 000.
How much money does Anjali have now?

10 Show how you can use the numbers **400, 150, 2000** and **251** to make the number 1999 by adding and subtracting.

2

Add your way through these number chains to copy and complete the empty boxes.

1
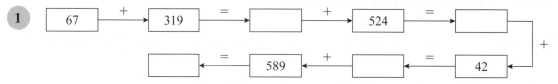

2
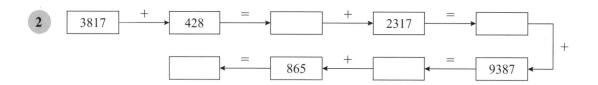

3
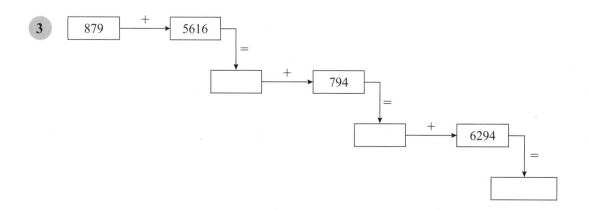

4 Marco has saved £22 650, Kelly has £3642 and Toni has £63 954. How much money do they have in total?

5 Joel has £28 300 and spends £9560 on a new car. How much money has Joel got left?

6 Carly has 1200 newsletters to deliver. When she returns home she has 304 newsletters left. How many newsletters has she delivered?

7 Work out 38 792 483 + 6 589 594

8 Copy and complete the addition square.

+		10		70
				490
653	753			
	299		599	
		5136		

HWK 3M ———————————————————— **Main Book page 4**

1 Increase 358 by 74.

2 What is the sum of 598 and 617?

3 Find the difference between 78 and 216.

4 Find the total of 603, 93 and 476.

5 Decrease 350 by 170.

6 Subtract 83 from 324.

7 Adding the numbers down gives the same total as adding the numbers across.
Find the missing number.

	968	
1680	2395	846
	?	

8 Cho has £793 less than Molly. If Molly has £3240, how much money does Cho have?

9 A (4287)　　　B (3619)　　　C (4934)

   a Find the difference between A and B, then find the difference between A and C.

   b Which is the larger difference and by how much?

10 Colin and Helen are saving to buy a flat which costs £135 000. Colin has £39 600 and Helen has £47 300. How much more money do they need to save?

11 Tanya spent £419 and has £73 left. How much money did she have to start with?

12 49 + 183 − 64

13 516 + 684 − 329

14 346 + 621 + 39 − 438

15 1714 − 239 − 87

Copy and complete

16 ☐ is 532 less than 829

17 ☐ subtract 168 is 487

18 5834 plus ☐ is 8120

19 ☐ decreased by 437 is 79

20 The number in each box is the sum of the numbers in the two boxes below.
Copy and complete each diagram.

a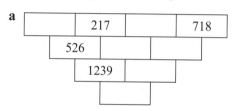

b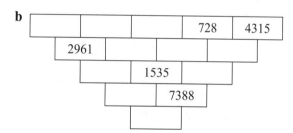

HWK 4M ———————————————————————— **Main Book page 6**

1 Copy and complete the grid.

×	4	9	3	7	11	8	5	12	0	6
6										
8			24							
9										
4										
7										

2 Copy and complete these multiplication squares.

a

×		7		4
				32
6	30			
4			36	
				36

b

×		3		
			88	
		21		35
	36			45
6			48	

c

×			6		
			36		
		18			
		42			
			45	10	
	72	27			

d

×					
			36	45	
			21		15
			56		64
		24			
		42	49		

HWK 5M ———————————————————————— **Main Book page 7**

Work out

1 273×9 **2** 524×6 **3** 746×5 **4** 387×8

5
$$8615 \times 6$$

6
$$7146 \times 8$$

7
$$4063 \times 7$$

8
$$37\,519 \times 8$$

9 A farmer has 139 hens. If each hen lays 6 eggs, how many eggs do the hens lay in total?

10 A shop sells 8 televisions at £799 each. How much money does the shop get for all 8 televisions?

11 How many days are there in 63 weeks?

6

12 Which is larger and by how much?

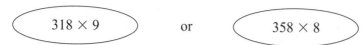

318×9 or 358×8

13 A pack of chews contains 47 sweets. Carly buys 4 packs, Tom buys 2 packs and Serena buys 3 packs. How many sweets do the three children have altogether?

14 Each class in Year 7 has 28 pupils. There are 8 classes. Each class in Year 8 has 27 pupils. There are 9 classes. How many pupils are there in Years 7 and 8 altogether?

15 2016 was a leap year. How many hours were there in February 2016?

16 Sam earns £913 each month. How much does Sam earn in nine months?

17 Given that $435 \times 47 = 20\,445$, work out 437×47 without multiplying.

18 Given that $517 \times 28 = 14\,476$, explain how this can be used to work out 527×28 without multiplying.

HWK 6M Main Book page 8

Copy and complete these number chains.

1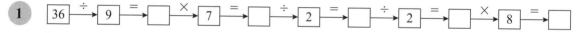

2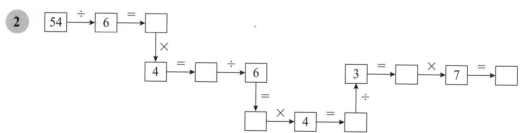

3

4 Copy and complete

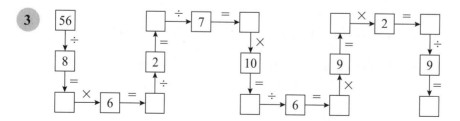

a $(6 + \square) \div 3 = 5$ **b** $(23 + \square) \div 8 = 6$ **c** $(67 - \square) \div 5 = 7$

d $(81 - \square) \div 7 = 8$ **e** $(27 + \square) \div 8 = 10$ **f** $(116 - \square) \div 6 = 9$

5 What number, when multiplied by 9 and then divided by 3, gives an answer of 6?

6 What number, when divided by 8 and then multiplied by 7, gives 56?

7 What number, when divided by 6 and then multiplied by 11, gives 99?

8 Work out

    a 4466 ÷ 7   **b** 4113 ÷ 9   **c** 3928 ÷ 8   **d** 5565 ÷ 7

9 Which is larger and by how much?

     or

10 £4578 is shared equally between 6 people. How much money does each person get?

11 A teacher divides 153 pencils equally between 9 children. How many pencils does each child get?

12 Is 2569 ÷ 7 larger than 352? If so, by how much?

13 A factory makes 4110 toys to sell for Christmas. The toys are delivered to shops in 6 equal lorry loads. How many toys go in each lorry?

14 Work out 40 947 445 ÷ 7

HWK 7M   **Main Book page 10**

1 Which division gives the larger remainder and by how much?

   or

2 Write each answer with a remainder.

    a 7)3140   **b** 4)58 375   **c** 6)597 183   **d** 6)283 174

In these questions, think carefully about whether you should round *up* or *down*.

3 30 children want to play football. How many full teams of 7 players can be made?

4 A taxi can carry 5 people. How many taxis are needed to carry 32 people?

5 A cinema ticket costs £6. How many tickets can be bought for £50?

6 An egg box holds 6 eggs. How many boxes do you need for 304 eggs?

7 How many 7 pence chews can I buy with £2?

8 9 children can sleep in a large tent. How many tents are needed for 110 children?

9 a How many Thunderbird 1 models can I buy with £150?
    b How many Thunderbird 2 models can I buy with £212?

Models	
£8	Thunderbird 1
£7	Thunderbird 2
£4	Thunderbird 4

10 Pencils are packed into boxes of 8. How many boxes are filled completely if you have 573 pencils?

11 How many 6 cm pieces of wood can be cut from a 2 metre piece of wood?

12 A charity puts £3 into each Christmas gift box. How many gift boxes can be done in this way if the charity has £6500?

HWK 8M   **Main Book page 11**

Use any method to work out the questions below.

1 53×46 **2** 62×37 **3** 47×78 **4** 94×53

5 74×436 **6** 825×64 **7** 237×182 **8** 649×328

9 In a school assembly there are 12 rows of chairs. Each row has 23 chairs. How many chairs are there in total?

10 a Danny is a decorator. He buys 24 pots of blue paint and 29 pots of yellow paint. How much does this cost in total?

   b 'SPLASH' painters buy 38 pots of blue, 23 pots of pink, 49 pots of yellow and 34 pots of red paint. How much do they spend in total?

Paint cost per pot		
5*l*	pink	£12
5*l*	blue	£13
10*l*	red	£21
10*l*	yellow	£23

11 Carla earns £23 per hour. One month she works for 152 hours. Ben earns £21 per hour. During the month he works 5 days each week for 4 weeks. On each day he works for 8 hours. Who earns the most money during this month and by how much?

12 A party of 347 people travel to the Olympic Games. Each person pays £78. How much money do these people pay in total?

Work out these questions. There are no remainders.

1 $6\overline{)882}$ **2** $14\overline{)588}$ **3** $13\overline{)689}$ **4** $23\overline{)575}$

5 $672 \div 42$ **6** $1377 \div 27$ **7** $1404 \div 39$ **8** $2772 \div 44$

9 $629 \div 37$ **10** $1216 \div 19$ **11** $1728 \div 48$ **12** $2492 \div 28$

Work out these questions. There may be remainders.

1 $285 \div 16$ **2** $416 \div 28$ **3** $739 \div 19$ **4** $624 \div 36$

5 Each box of matches contains 43 matches. How many boxes can be filled from 750 matches?

6 There are 28 children in a class. The teacher has 402 sweets and wants to give each child the same number of sweets. What is the greatest number of sweets a child gets and how many sweets are left over?

7 A bus can carry 57 people. How many buses are needed to carry 765 people?

8 Copy and complete

a $\boxed{} \times 34 = 1224$ b $1431 \div 53 = \boxed{}$ c $47 \times \boxed{} = 3149$

9 A school needs 450 rulers. They are sold in packs of 24. How many packs will the school need to order? How many extra rulers will there be?

10 How many 34p stamps can be bought with £5 and how much money will be left over?

1.2 Decimals

1 What does the digit 4 in 8.427 represent? And the 2? And the 7?

2 Write down nine hundredths as a decimal number.

3 Write down seventeen hundredths as a decimal number.

4 Which is the larger of each pair of numbers below?

a 0.6 or 0.62

b 0.523 or 0.533

c 0.28 or 0.82

d 0.9 or 0.009

e 5.7 or 5.07

f 0.8 or 0.75

g 0.09 or $\dfrac{7}{10}$

h 4 or 4.00

i 3.04 or 3.3

j $\dfrac{8}{100}$ or 0.7

5 Give the value of each underlined digit $\left(\text{e.g. } 1.8\underline{6}: \dfrac{6}{100}\right)$

a 7.9$\underline{3}$

b 1.$\underline{4}$

c 9.$\underline{3}$7

d $\underline{4}$9.63

e 513.2$\underline{6}$

6 Two chefs use 2.7 kg of flour and 1.8 kg of flour. They had 5 kg of flour to start with.

a How much flour do they use in total?

b How much flour do they have left?

7 Write down the next three terms in each sequence.

a 0.7 0.9 1.1 1.3

b 0.2 0.8 1.4

c 2.4 2.1 1.8 1.5

8 Find the missing number in each question below.

a 7.53 + ? = 7.73

b 0.816 − ? = 0.616

c ? + 5.143 = 5.149

d 12.327 − ? = 12.027

9 Terry weighs 44.535 kg. Two weeks later he weighs 44.235 kg. How much weight has he lost?

HWK 2M ──────────────────────────────── **Main Book page 19**

1 Write the numbers in order of size, smallest first.

a 0.48, 0.28, 0.33

b 0.19, 0.34, 0.2

c 0.12, 0.03, 0.1

d 0.92, 0.925, 0.903

e 0.68, 0.73, 0.7, 0.62

f 9.399, 9.31, 9.2, 9.36

g 0.307, 0.4, 0.08, 0.24

h 0.4, 0.53, 0.52, 0.501

2 Increase 9.32 by $\dfrac{1}{10}$

3 Increase 7.287 by $\dfrac{1}{1000}$

4 Six sprinters in a 200 m race ran the following times (in seconds):

| Matt 26.3 | Dan 26.27 | Sunil 26.41 | Tom 26.19 | Alex 26.4 | Carl 26.24 |

a Who won the race?

b Write down the names in the order that they finished.

5 Julia ran 0.3 km, Suraj ran 285 m and Chun ran $\frac{2}{5}$ km. Who ran the shortest distance? Explain your answer fully.

HWK 3M ———————————————————— **Main Book page 20**

Work out the value indicated by each arrow.

1 0 — 1 **2** 3 — 4 **3** 1 — 2.5

4 7 — 8 **5** 2 — 2.04 **6** 0 — 0.1

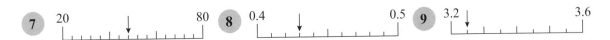

7 20 — 80 **8** 0.4 — 0.5 **9** 3.2 — 3.6

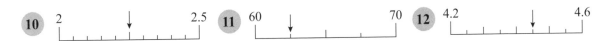

10 2 — 2.5 **11** 60 — 70 **12** 4.2 — 4.6

13 7 — 8 **14** 6 — 6.5 **15** 17 — 18

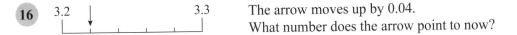

16 3.2 — 3.3   The arrow moves up by 0.04.
What number does the arrow point to now?

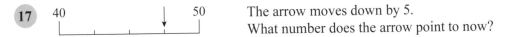

17 40 — 50   The arrow moves down by 5.
What number does the arrow point to now?

18 2.6 — 2.65   The arrow moves up by 0.03.
What number does the arrow point to now?

19 Arrow A (opposite) points to the amount of petrol in a car tank. Mr Amos uses the car. Arrow B points to how much petrol is in the car after Mr Amos has used it. How much petrol did Mr Amos use?

0   B   A   40 litres

HWK 4M ———————————————————— **Main Book page 21**

Work out

1   8.72
      + 4.91

2   17
      + 3.6

3   16.4
      − 13.6

4   6
      − 4.3

5 $9 - 6.8$

6 $0.3 + 5 + 2.14$

7 $17.6 + 3.82 + 4$

8 $16.4 - 11.7$

9 $5.4 - 2.16$

10 $19 - 5.82$

11 Find the number which belongs in each empty box.

    a $1.8 + \boxed{} = 3.25$ **b** $\boxed{} + 1.87 = 12$

    c $2.9 - \boxed{} = 1.17$ **d** $\boxed{} - 0.58 = 7.6$

12 Didier bought a burger for £2.33, a drink for 78p and an ice cream for £1.10. How much change did he have from a £10 note?

13 Jasmine bought a shirt for £21.89 and some trousers for £29.50. Alonso spent £33.45 on a sweatshirt and £18.10 on swimming trunks. Who spent the most and by how much?

14

CAFÉ ROUGE			
tea	95p	chips	90p
coffee	£1.10	sandwich	£1.87
coke	85p	pizza	£4.19
lemonade	70p	fish	£2.75
orange juice	£1.15	burger	£1.65

Cassie and Shane go to the Café Rouge.

    a Cassie wants to buy a pizza and coke. She has £5. Does she have enough money?

    b Shane has £10. He lends Cassie the extra money she needs and also buys an orange juice. How much money does Shane have left?

15 Find the number which belongs in each empty box.

    a $\boxed{} + 0.072 = 0.115$ **b** $\boxed{} - 0.006 = 5.735$

    c $\boxed{} - 0.049 = 9.689$ **d** $14.624 - \boxed{} = 0.378$

16 Aidan subtracts 0.07 from 3.24 and gets the answer 3.23. *Explain clearly* what mistake you think Aidan has made.

17 I can walk to a shop and buy a radio for £27.85 and some headphones for £8.99. In a second shop I can buy the radio for £25.99 and the headphones for £6.75. How much do I save by going to the second shop if the return bus fare is £2.15?

18 Maya raises £810.76 for a charity by doing a sponsored walk, a card sale and a prize raffle. She makes £512.12 from the sponsored walk and £213.68 from the prize raffle. How much money does she make from the card sale?

Copy and complete the following

1   6.2 $\xrightarrow{\times 100}$ ☐ $\xrightarrow{\times 10}$ ☐ $\xrightarrow{\div 100}$ ☐

2   0.8 $\xrightarrow{\times 100}$ ☐ $\xrightarrow{\div 10}$ ☐ $\xrightarrow{\times 100}$ ☐

3   37 $\xrightarrow{\div 10}$ ☐ $\xrightarrow{\times 100}$ ☐ $\xrightarrow{\div 10}$ ☐

4   ☐ $\xrightarrow{\div 100}$ 4.83 $\xrightarrow{\times 10}$ ☐ $\xrightarrow{\times 100}$ ☐

5   ☐ $\xrightarrow{\times 100}$ ☐ $\xrightarrow{\div 10}$ 89 $\xrightarrow{\div 100}$ ☐

6   ☐ $\xrightarrow{\div 10}$ ☐ $\xrightarrow{\times 10}$ ☐ $\xrightarrow{\div 100}$ 0.2

7   ☐ $\xrightarrow{\times 100}$ ☐ $\xrightarrow{\div 1000}$ 0.61 $\xrightarrow{\times 10}$ ☐

8   ☐ $\xrightarrow{\times 1000}$ 834 $\xrightarrow{\div 10}$ ☐ $\xrightarrow{\times 100}$ ☐

9   ☐ $\xrightarrow{\times 100}$ ☐ $\xrightarrow{\div 10}$ ☐ $\xrightarrow{\div 100}$ 9.3

10   ☐ $\xrightarrow{\div 10}$ ☐ $\xrightarrow{\times 100}$ 119 $\xrightarrow{\div 1000}$ ☐

Work out the following. Check each answer by estimating.

11 2.7×6 **12** 0.14×3 **13** 4.81×5 **14** 8×0.53

15 12.3×9 **16** 4×3.46 **17** 0.95×3 **18** 17.2×6

19   A computer game costs £8.65 in a second-hand shop. How much would 5 of these games cost in this shop?

20   What is the cost of 8 scarves at £9.85 each?

21   Find each missing number.

    a $0.7 \times \boxed{} = 3.5$ **b** $\boxed{} \times 8 = 4.8$ **c** $\boxed{} \times 0.15 = 0.45$ **d** $7 \times \boxed{} = 0.21$

HWK 6M ──────────────────────────────── **Main Book page 24**

1 Copy and complete

a $\boxed{} \times 0.07 = 7$

b $\boxed{} \times 10 = 32$

c $\boxed{} \times 100 = 946$

d $0.8 \times \boxed{} = 800$

e $\boxed{} \times 100 = 14.4$

f $371 \div \boxed{} = 37.1$

g $42 \div \boxed{} = 0.42$

h $\boxed{} \div 10 = 0.8$

i $\boxed{} \div 100 = 5.71$

2 Find the total cost of 6 pineapples at £1.84 each.

3 A tin of soup weighs 0.47 kg. How much will 9 tins weigh?

4 If 1 kg equals 2.2 pounds, how many pounds does a 5 kg sack of potatoes weigh?

5 How much does Sonia spend on this shopping?

> 5 tins of beans at £0.49 each
>
> 3 pints of milk at 47p per pint
>
> 1 loaf of bread at £1.06

6 How much change from £30 will Dylan get when he buys this shopping?

> 2 boxes of cereal at £1.93 per box
>
> $\frac{1}{2}$ kg of apples at 92p per kg
>
> 3 bottles of wine at £7.14 per bottle
>
> 6 bags of crisps at 38p per bag

7 Copy and complete

a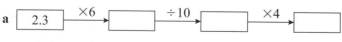

2.3 $\xrightarrow{\times 6}$ $\boxed{}$ $\xrightarrow{\div 10}$ $\boxed{}$ $\xrightarrow{\times 4}$ $\boxed{}$

b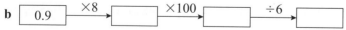

0.9 $\xrightarrow{\times 8}$ $\boxed{}$ $\xrightarrow{\times 100}$ $\boxed{}$ $\xrightarrow{\div 6}$ $\boxed{}$

c

0.07 $\xrightarrow{\times 4}$ $\boxed{}$ $\xrightarrow{\times 10}$ $\boxed{}$ $\xrightarrow{\div 2}$ $\boxed{}$

8 A shirt costs £22.50. Each shirt is given a logo for an extra £6.15. A school buys 20 shirts with logos. What is the total cost?

9 Aaliyah says that 19.8×5.1 is equal to 100.98. Seb says that 20×5 is equal to 100 so Aaliyah is probably correct. Do you think that this is a sensible statement from Seb? *Explain* your answer fully.

10 If $168 \times 24 = 4032$, write down the value of 16.8×2.4.

HWK 7M ——————————————————————————————— **Main Book page 26**

1 Work out

 a 0.6×0.4 **b** 0.8×0.07 **c** 6×0.09 **d** 0.9×8

 e 7×0.05 **f** 0.02×0.3 **g** 16×0.04 **h** 0.8×21

 i 1.8×0.6 **j** 0.07×0.04 **k** 0.32×0.5 **l** 0.003×1.3

2 Cheddar cheese costs £4.20 per kg. Ken buys 0.6 kg of cheese. How much does Ken pay?

3 A table at a local snooker club costs £5.30 per hour to hire. Simon and Denise play snooker for 1 hour 24 minutes. How much do they pay for the table? (1 hour 24 minutes = 1.4 hours)

4 Copy and complete

 a $7 \times 0.03 = \boxed{}$ **b** $0.8 \times \boxed{} = 0.16$ **c** $0.04 \times \boxed{} = 0.28$

 d $\boxed{} \times 0.6 = 0.042$ **e** $\boxed{} \times 0.03 = 0.012$ **f** $0.07 \times \boxed{} = 6.3$

5 Explain why a number gets smaller if it is multiplied by 0.1

6 Work out 8.69×0.47

HWK 8M ——————————————————————————————— **Main Book page 27**

Work out

1 $18.6 \div 6$ **2** $60.8 \div 8$ **3** $7.6 \div 4$ **4** $26.6 \div 7$

5 $194.4 \div 9$ **6** $12.84 \div 3$ **7** $25.95 \div 5$ **8** $51.2 \div 4$

9 $41.4 \div 5$ **10** $226.1 \div 7$ **11** $108.2 \div 5$ **12** $71.12 \div 8$

13 A sheet of metal weighing 51.2 kg is to be divided into 8 equal parts. How much will each part weigh?

14 10.7 litres of paint are poured equally into 5 tins. How much paint is in each tin?

15 Work out

    a $11 \div 4$ **b** $25.8 \div 8$ **c** $27.25 \div 5$ **d** $12.368 \div 2$

    e $66 \div 8$ **f** $65 \div 4$ **g** $113.2 \div 4$ **h** $0.16 \div 5$

16 Each of 3 triplets weigh the same amount. If their total weight is 154.8 kg, how much do each of the triplets weigh?

17 The total bill for a meal is £131.04. Seven people agree to pay an equal share. How much does each person pay?

1.3 Using a calculator

HWK 1M	Main Book page 33

Work out

1 $8 - 3 \times 2$ **2** $5 + 4 \times 3$ **3** $7 + 4 \times 6$

4 $3 \times 5 + 4$ **5** $7 \times 9 - 9$ **6** $8 \times 6 - 7$

7 $7 + 12 \div 3$ **8** $8 + 16 \div 2$ **9** $15 - 9 \div 3$

10 $30 \div 6 + 7$ **11** $45 \div 9 - 4$ **12** $28 + 4 \times 11$

13 $15 + 28 \div 7$ **14** $7 \times 8 + 17$ **15** $54 \div 6 - 5$

16 Copy and fill in each box to give the correct answer.

    a $5 \times \boxed{} + 2 = 22$ **b** $\boxed{} \times 7 - 6 = 15$ **c** $6 + 10 \div \boxed{} = 8$

    d $\boxed{} + 3 \times 8 = 29$ **e** $(8 - \boxed{}) \times 7 = 28$ **f** $15 \div (1 + \boxed{}) = 3$

    g $30 \div \boxed{} + 4 = 9$ **h** $(\boxed{} + 8) \times 6 = 66$ **i** $16 + 18 \div \boxed{} = 25$

17 Work out

    a $0.2 + 0.2 \times 0.3$ **b** $1.4 + 2.1 \div 7$ **c** $3 - 0.4 \times 0.5$

HWK 2M	Main Book page 34

Work out

1 $3 + 5 \times 7 + 4$ **2** $28 - 3 \times 6 + 4$ **3** $5 + 20 \div 5 + 3$

4 $12 - 30 \div 6 - 2$ **5** $27 \div 9 + 3 \times 6$ **6** $42 \div 7 - 36 \div 6$

7 $48 - 6 \times 7 + 9$

8 $8 \times 9 \div 3 + 7$

9 $7 \times 9 - 54 \div 9$

10 $(8 - 2) \times 8$

11 $56 \div (9 - 2)$

12 $(6 + 4) \times (15 - 8)$

13 $(13 + 11) \div (12 - 6)$

14 $9 \times (24 - 15)$

15 $5 \times 9 - 4 \times 7$

16 $72 \div 8 + 3 \times 7$

17 $(14 + 6) \times (7 - 4)$

18 $17 + 49 \div 7 - 16$

19 $200 - (36 \div 3)$

20 $40 \div 8 + 4 \times 9$

21 $7 \times 6 + (120 - 39)$

22 $1.8 + 0.3 \times 0.6 + 0.9$

23 $6.3 \div (2 + 5)$

24 $2.5 \times 0.2 - 0.8 \times 0.4$

HWK 3M — Main Book page 35

Copy each question and write brackets so that each calculation gives the correct answer.

1 $4 + 3 \times 6 = 42$

2 $5 \times 4 - 1 = 15$

3 $7 + 5 \times 6 = 37$

4 $56 \div 10 - 2 = 7$

5 $5 \times 4 + 2 \times 6 = 32$

6 $8 \times 7 - 2 - 9 = 31$

7 $13 + 12 \div 5 = 5$

8 $18 + 18 - 8 \div 4 = 7$

9 $4 \times 6 + 9 - 5 = 40$

10 $42 - 6 \times 6 = 6$

11 $15 + 6 \times 3 + 7 = 40$

12 $24 - 9 \div 27 \div 9 = 5$

13 $41 + 22 \div 3 + 6 = 7$

14 $8 + 10 \times 0 + 6 = 6$

15 $58 - 4 \div 48 \div 8 = 9$

16 Write down the difference between the answers to the two questions below:

$36 - (6 \div 2)$ and $(36 - 6) \div 2$

17 Jamie writes $8 \times (6 - 3) \times 3 = 72$. Is he correct?
If not, explain what mistake he has made.

HWK 3E — Main Book page 35

$(7 - 3) \times 8 = 32$ so the answer 32 can be found by using the numbers 7, 3 and 8.

For each question below, use each number once to give the correct answer.
Write down the calculation each time.

1 8, 6 and 3 to give answer 6

2 7, 3 and 6 to give answer 60

3 5, 3 and 9 to give answer 30

4 10, 32 and 2 to give answer 4

5 9, 8 and 4 to give answer 44

6 3, 10 and 7 to give answer 100

7 4, 48 and 12 to give answer 6

8 64, 6 and 2 to give answer 8

9 3, 9 and 5 to give answer 72

10 28, 3 and 21 to give answer 4

11 5, 2, 20 and 1 to give answer 3

12 2, 3, 5 and 9 to give answer 42

13 Make up five questions of your own like these. You may use as many numbers as you like. Try them on other people in your next lesson.

HWK 4M   **Main Book page 36**

1 Does $18 - (6 \div 3)$ equal $\dfrac{18 - 6}{3}$ or $18 - \dfrac{6}{3}$?

2 The answers for $2 + \dfrac{1.5}{0.25}$ and $\dfrac{2 + 1.5}{0.25}$ are 14 and 8. Which answer belongs to which calculation?

Use a calculator to work out

3 $5.3 + \dfrac{18.27}{2.9}$

4 $3.92 + 4.3 \times 2.6$

5 $\dfrac{6.41 + 9.55}{3.8}$

6 $\dfrac{1.9 \times 2.4}{0.04}$

7 $4.6 + \dfrac{27.44}{4.9}$

8 $\dfrac{29.732 - 3.94}{4.16}$

9 $7.16 - \dfrac{35.1}{7.8}$

10 $4.8 + 2.6 \times 2.9$

11 $\dfrac{8.513 + 3.793}{8.79}$

12 Polly buys 3 magazines at £2.95 each and 4 bottles of water at £1.07 each. How much does she spend in total?

13 Tom weighs 13 stone. Each stone is 14 pounds. Tom is a 'good' weight if he weighs less than 190 pounds. Is Tom a 'good' weight?

14 Explain which fraction buttons could be used on a calculator for the sum

$$8.2 + 15 \div 2.5 + 28 \div 3.5$$

15 Use a calculator to work out

$$\dfrac{6.2 + 4.3944}{3.23} - \dfrac{17.064}{7.9}$$

HWK 5M ———————————————————————— **Main Book page 37**

Use a calculator to complete this crossnumber.

1		2			3	
				4		
5			6			
		7		8		9
10						
11	12		13			
14						

Across

1. $\dfrac{1505}{0.2} - 39$

3. $(0.15 + 0.35) \times (70 - 8)$

4. $(2.19 - 0.44) \times 8$

5. $1172.5 + (10\,251 \div 2)$

7. $\dfrac{12\,105}{0.4} + \dfrac{137\,052}{8}$

11. $(4 + 5) \times 4$

13. $3 \times (893.5 + 516.5) + 909$

14. $15\,455 \div (3.719 - 1.219)$

Down

1. $179 \times (2.16 + 1.84)$

2. $19\,445 + \dfrac{37\,500}{(0.7 - 0.1)}$

3. $\dfrac{2458}{(0.61 + 0.19)} + \dfrac{2852}{(3.2 + 4.8)}$

6. $290 \times (0.08 + 0.22)$

8. $(24.8 - 8.72 + 2.92) \times 19$

9. $(2107 + 1324) \times 2 - 1966$

10. $\dfrac{(113 + 96)}{(0.5 \times 0.5)}$

12. $\dfrac{(13.2 + 1.8)}{(0.29 - 0.04)} + 1$

13. $\dfrac{41.6}{0.8}$

20

1.4 Rules of algebra

In questions **1** to **8** write down the expression that you obtain.

1   I start with a number x then subtract 13.

2   I start with a number y then multiply it by 4.

3   I start with a number m, double it then add 6.

4   I start with a number p, multiply it by 5 then take away 3.

5   I start with a number w, multiply it by 9 then add 15.

6   I start with a number B then divide it by 4.

7   I start with a number A, multiply it by 7 then subtract 2.

8   I start with a number y, divide it by 10 then add 3.

9   Use algebra to write down the length of this piece of string.

10   A boy cycles b km and then another c km. How far does he cycle altogether?

11   Jim has x books. He gives 9 books to a jumble sale. How many books does he have now?

12   Fatima has n sweets. Her brother gives her 16 sweets. How many sweets does she have now?

13   Use algebra to find the perimeter p of this shape.

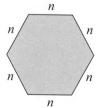

Use algebra to find the perimeter p of each shape in questions **14** to **16**.

14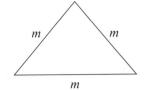

15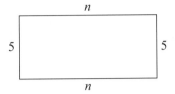

16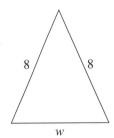

17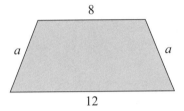

Valeria says that the perimeter
of this shape is $22a$.
Is she correct?
Give a reason for your answer.

18   **a** Draw a triangle and label the sides so that the perimeter is $6 + m$.

     b Draw a different triangle with a perimeter equal to $6 + m$.

HWK 1E ———————————————————————— **Main Book page 43**

In questions **1** to **8** write down the expression that you obtain.

1   I start with x, treble it then subtract y.

2   I start with m, double it then add p.

3   I start with q, subtract r then add 5.

4   I start with $2a$, add 7 then add b.

5   I start with $6n$, add $3p$ then subtract $4q$.

6   I subtract y from $4w$ and then add $7p$.

7   I add together $3f$, $2g$ and $6h$ then subtract 9.

8   I subtract $8b$ from $4a$ and then subtract $3c$.

9   Sandra has 38 marbles but loses x of them. How many marbles does Sandra now have?

10   ⟵——y cm——⟶   Nick eats 5 cm off one end of this piece of rock.
                                How long is the piece of rock that is left?

22

11 A bottle of water contains 2 litres. How many litres of water are contained in w bottles?

12 Josh has 89 pence. His sister lends him x pence and he spends m pence. How much money does he now have?

13 Terry has 3 times as many socks as Jack plus an extra 6 socks. If Jack has n socks, how many socks does Terry have?

14 A small bag of mints contains w mints. A large bag contains 4 times as many mints. Jo buys a large bag and eats 5 mints. How many mints are left in the bag?

15 Draw and label a shape whose perimeter p is given by the formula $p = 3n + 7$.

16 Draw and label a shape whose perimeter is equal to the perimeter of the shape shown opposite.

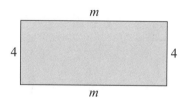

HWK 2M   **Main Book page 45**

Simplify the following expressions where possible.

1 $6b + 2b$ **2** $7x - 3x$ **3** $9a - 4b$ **4** $5m + m$

5 $7a + 3a$ **6** $6h - 2h$ **7** $8y - 7y$ **8** $4x + 7$

9 $8m + 1$ **10** $12x + 5x$ **11** $9p - 5$ **12** $13y + y$

13 $19b - 14b$ **14** $16m + 18m$ **15** $19a - a$ **16** $19a - 3$

17 $23n - 14n$ **18** $25n + 14$ **19** $5y + 2$ **20** $6q + 22q$

21 Gareth says that $4n + n$ is equal to $4n$. Is he correct? Give a reason for your answer.

22 Is $5n + 5n$ the same as $11n - n$? Give a reason for your answer.

HWK 3M   **Main Book page 46**

Simplify the following expressions as far as possible by collecting like terms.

1 $4m + 6n + 4m + 3n$ **2** $5p + 7q + 3p + 9q$ **3** $6a + 5b - 2a + 4b$

4 $8x + 12y - 6x - 9y$ **5** $16f + 19g + 6f - 12g$ **6** $7m + 9 + m - 6$

7 $2b + 6c + 5b - 4c$ **8** $9m + 8 - 2m - 7$ **9** $15 + 4y + 12 - 3y$

10 $6x + 15y - 10y + x$ **11** $4a + 23 + 7 - 2a$ **12** $11 + 5n - 7 + 2n$

13 $12w - 3w + 8 + 7$ **14** $13p + 19 - 9p - 2p$ **15** $16 + 12m - 3 + 12$

In questions **16** to **18** , copy and complete the number chains.

16

$3a \xrightarrow{+} 5b \xrightarrow{=} \boxed{} \xrightarrow{+} 7b \xrightarrow{} \boxed{} \xrightarrow{-} 2a \xrightarrow{=} \boxed{} \xrightarrow{+} 9a \xrightarrow{=} \boxed{}$

17

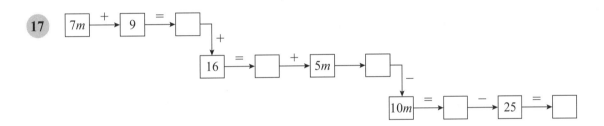

18

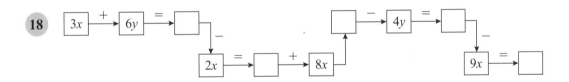

19 $16m + 9n + \boxed{} = 19m + 5n$ What belongs in the empty box?

20 $12x + 6y + \boxed{} = y$ What belongs in the empty box?

21 A piece of metal is $(7n + 8)$ cm long. It is cut into two parts. If one piece is $(5n + 3)$ cm long, how long is the other piece?

22 Liz is $(7m + 20)$ cm tall. Over the next six months she grows by $(m + 1)$ cm. Hector says she is $(7m + 21)$ cm tall now. By how many centimetres is Hector wrong with his answer?

23 $7a + 3b + a + 2b + 8$ equals $\boxed{8a + 5b + 8}$ or $\boxed{7a + 5b + 8}$

Which answer above is *not* correct? Explain clearly the mistake that has been made.

1   List the expressions below which are equal to $3n$.

$$\boxed{3 + n} \qquad \boxed{3 \times n} \qquad \boxed{n + n + n} \qquad \boxed{3 \div n}$$

$$\boxed{4n - n} \qquad \boxed{3 - n} \qquad \boxed{2n + n} \qquad \boxed{n \times 3}$$

2   **a** Write down any pairs of expressions from below that are equal to each other.

$$\boxed{6 - n} \qquad \boxed{4n + n} \qquad \boxed{\dfrac{3}{n}} \qquad \boxed{n + n}$$

$$\boxed{5 \times n} \qquad \boxed{\dfrac{n}{3}} \qquad \boxed{7n - 5n} \qquad \boxed{n - 6}$$

b For each chosen pair from part **a**, write down a value for n which shows that you are correct.

3   **a** List the expressions below which are equal to $2a + 3b$.

$$\boxed{a + a + b + b} \qquad \boxed{5a + 3b - 3} \qquad \boxed{3a + 3b - a} \qquad \boxed{2a + 2b + b}$$

$$\boxed{6a + b - 4a + 2b} \qquad \boxed{a + 4b - b + a} \qquad \boxed{2a + 2b + 1} \qquad \boxed{7a + 6b - 5a - 2b}$$

b For each expression you have chosen, use $a = 5$ and $b = 4$ to check that each one is equal to the value of $2a + 3b$.

4   Does $(5 + n)$ equal $(n + 5)$ for all values of n?
If so, show a value of n that works.

5   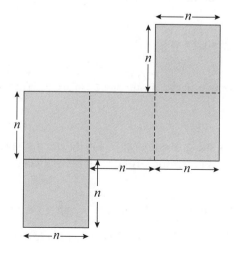 Write down an expression for the total area of this shape.

6 Hailey says that the area of this shape is $8n + 8n$, which equals $16n$. *Explain clearly* whether she is correct or not.

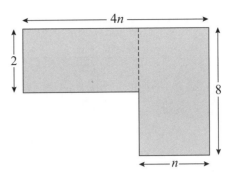

| HWK 5M | Main Book page 48 |

Simplify

1 $6m \times 3n$

2 $9p \times 4q$

3 $5y \times 5w$

4 $8a \times b$

5 $7m \times 5n$

6 $10x \times 4y$

7 Phil has $3n$ sweets. He eats n sweets then Alice gives him $2p$ sweets. Phil now eats $(n + p)$ sweets. How many sweets has he got left now?

8 Josie is $(5a + 7b)$ metres tall. Jack is $(4a + b)$ metres tall. How much taller is Josie than Jack? (we are assuming that Josie is taller)

9 What must be added to $3nm$ to give $9mn$?

In questions **10** to **24**, write down each statement and say whether it is 'true' or 'false'.

10 $4 \times m = 4m$

11 $x + x + x + x = 4x$

12 $n + 5 = 5 + n$

13 $a \times a = a^2$

14 $10 + w = 10w$

15 $8 - n = n - 8$

16 $mn = nm$

17 $b \div 4 = 4 \div b$

18 $2 \times y = y^2$

19 $x + y + x = 2x + y$

20 $m + n + p = mnp$

21 $\dfrac{a}{3} = \dfrac{3}{a}$

22 $5n - n = 5$

23 $w \times 9 = 9w$

24 $3y + 5 = 8y$

25 Colton says that $8a \times 7b = 56ab$ and Mila says that $8a \times 7b = 56ba$. Who is correct? Give a reason for your answer.

26 Find an expression for the total area of these three rectangles.

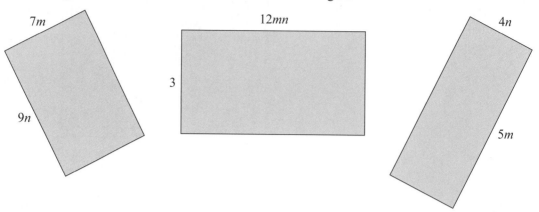

| **HWK 6M** | **Main Book page 51** |

1 The perimeter p of this hexagon is given by the formula $p = 6a$.
Find p when $a = 4$.

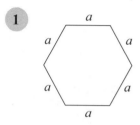

2 The perimeter p of a rectangle with sides m and n is given by the formula $p = 2m + 2n$.
Find p when $m = 7$ and $n = 3$.

3

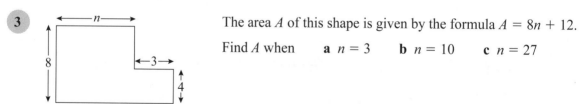

The area A of this shape is given by the formula $A = 8n + 12$.

Find A when   **a** $n = 3$ **b** $n = 10$ **c** $n = 27$

4 The perimeter p of a shape is given by the formula $p = 5n + 17$. Find p when $n = 8$.

5 The area A of a parallelogram is given by the formula $A = bh$, where b is the base of the parallelogram and h is its height. Find A when $b = 24$ and $h = 7$.

6 The area A of a shape is given by the formula $A = 4x + 3y$. Layla works out the area A when $x = 2$ and $y = 7$. Her working out is shown below.

$A = 4x + 3y$
$A = 7xy$
$A = 7 \times 2 \times 7$
$A = 98$

Is Layla correct? If not, explain what mistake she made.

7 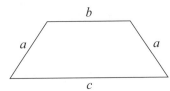 A formula for the perimeter p of this trapezium is

$$p = 2a + b + c$$

Find p when $a = 12$, $b = 19$ and $c = 33$.

8 The area A of a shape is given by the formula

$$A = 7x + 15$$

Find A when **a** $x = 2$ **b** $x = 32$ **c** $x = 101$

HWK 6E	**Main Book page 52**

A formula is given in each question. Find the value of the letter required in each case.

1 $m = 2n + 9$ Find m when $n = 6$

2 $b = 2c - 5$ Find b when $c = 8$

3 $a = 23 - b$ Find a when $b = 16$

4 $w = 33 - 4y$ Find w when $y = 5$

5 $f = \dfrac{h}{8}$ Find f when $h = 56$

6 $y = 5(x + 3)$ Find y when $x = 6$

7 $a = bc$ Find a when $b = 3$, $c = 12$

8 $k = \dfrac{m}{9} + 13$ Find k when $m = 72$

9 $p = 7(28 - q)$ Find p when $q = 19$

10 $y = x(x - 4)$ Find y when $x = 15$

11 $m = 8np$ Find m when $n = 2$, $p = 6$

12 $a = b^2$ Find a when $b = 12$

13 $d = \dfrac{e}{7} - 6$ Find d when $e = 49$

14 $v = w(w + y)$ Find v when $w = 8$, $y = 5$

15 $y = xw - x$ Find y when $x = 11$, $w = 4$

16 $m = n^2 + p^2 - t^2$
Find m when $n = 6$, $p = 20$, $t = 8$

17 The volume V of the box shown opposite is given by the formula

$$V = 3x^2$$

Find the value of V if $x = 2$.

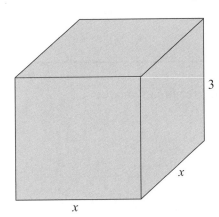

28

Find the value of the required symbol.

1   Find ▽ if ☆ = 18.

2   Find ▽ if ⌒ = 15.

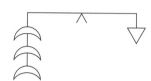

3   Find ☆ if ⌒ = 12.

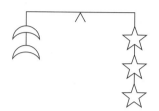

4   Find ⌒ if ▽ = 20.

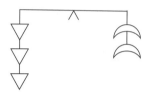

5   Find ⌒ if ☆ = 18.

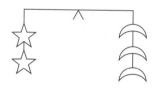

6   Find ☆ if ▽ = 9.

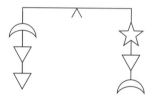

7   Find ▽ if ⌒ = 30.

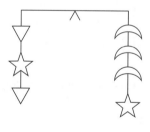

8   Find ⌒ if ☆ = 10.

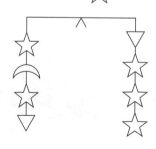

9   Find ☆ if ⌒ = 9.

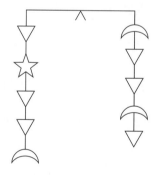

Find the value of the required symbol.

1   Find ⌒ and ▽ if ☆ = 18.

2   Find ⌒ and ☆ if ▽ = 28.

29

3 Find ▽ and ⌢ if ☆ = 12.

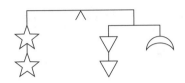

4 Find ▽ and ☆ if ⌢ = 10.

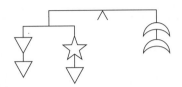

5 Find ☆ and ⌢ if ▽ = 6.

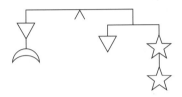

6 Find ⌢ and ☆ if ▽ = 8.

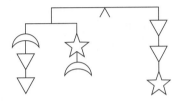

7 Find ☆ and ▽ if ⌢ = 14.

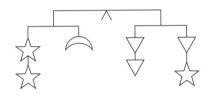

8 Find ☆ and ▽ if ⌢ = 12.

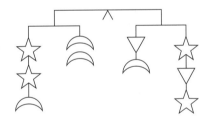

9 Find ☆ and ⌢ if ▽ = 20.

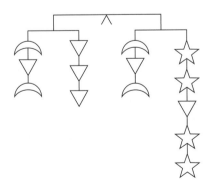

10 Find ⌢ and ▽ if ☆ = 30.

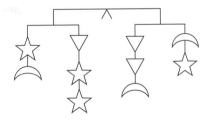

1.5 Negative numbers

HWK 1M   **Main Book page 60**

1 $-10\ -9\ -8\ -7\ -6\ -5\ -4\ -3\ -2\ -1\ \ 0\ \ 1\ \ 2\ \ 3\ \ 4\ \ 5\ \ 6\ \ 7\ \ 8\ \ 9\ \ 10$

Find the difference between

a -6 and 2   b -7 and -2 c -4 and 3

2 Which temperature is the coldest? $-3°C$ $0°C$ $-5°C$

3 The temperature in Nottingham is $-2°$ C.

a What is the temperature if it rises by $6°$ C?

b What is the temperature if it drops by $2°$ C?

4 The temperature in Cardiff is $11°$ C. What is the new temperature if it falls by $14°$ C?

5 Write down these temperatures in order, coldest first.

a $6°$ C, $-2°$ C, $-4°$ C, $1°$ C, $-7°$ C, $2°$ C

b $0°$ C, $-8°$ C, $-3°$ C, $5°$ C, $-5°$ C, $-1°$ C

6 The temperature in Glasgow is $-6°$ C. The temperature in Gloucester is $3°$ C. What is the difference in the temperatures?

7 John has a bank balance of $-£150$ (this means he owes £150). What is his bank balance if he pays in £100?

8 Write down true or false for each statement below.

a $-3 > -2$ b $-6 < -7$ c $0 < -3$ d $-4 > -6$

($>$ means 'is greater than' and $<$ means 'is less than')

9 What number is exactly half way between -16 and 10?

10 *Explain* why $-3 + 5$ is equal to 2.

HWK 2M   **Main Book page 62**

1 $-10\ -9\ -8\ -7\ -6\ -5\ -4\ -3\ -2\ -1\ \ 0\ \ 1\ \ 2\ \ 3\ \ 4\ \ 5\ \ 6\ \ 7\ \ 8\ \ 9\ \ 10$

Work out

a $-6 + 2$ b $-4 + 3$ c $4 - 7$ d $-5 + 3$

e $3 - 8$ f $-2 - 1$ g $-4 - 3$ h $-6 + 4$

2 Work out

   a $-9 + 3$ **b** $6 - 10$ **c** $-5 - 3$ **d** $-4 + 11$

   e $-1 - 6$ **f** $-7 + 5$ **g** $-3 + 3$ **h** $-2 - 8$

3 Which of these sums give the answer in the middle?

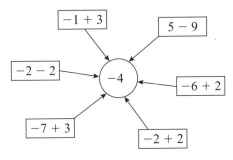

4 Work out

   a $5 - 2 - 6$ **b** $4 + 1 - 8$ **c** $-3 - 2 + 1$

   d $-4 + 3 - 4$ **e** $6 - 4 - 4$ **f** $-5 - 2 + 3$

5 Find the missing number.

    $-4 + 2 - 3 + ? = -1$

6 If $-2 - 2 - 2 = -6$, what does $-2 - 2 - 2 - 2$ equal?

7 Work out

    $-9 + 5 + 2 - 3 - 1 + 4$

8 Copy and complete each empty box.

   a $-5 + \square = 1$ **b** $-3 - \square = -5$ **c** $-8 - \square = -12$

   d $4 - \square = -7$ **e** $-10 + \square = -4$ **f** $-2 - \square + 3 = 0$

9 Which calculation below gives the larger answer and by how much?

    $\boxed{-9 + 2}$ or $\boxed{-1 - 7}$

10 Work out

    $-8 + 2 - 4 - 1 + 5 + 2 - 3$

HWK 3M ────────────────────────────────── **Main Book page 64**

1 Work out

a $6 - (-4)$ b $5 + (-3)$ c $3 - (-9)$ d $-2 + (-3)$

e $-1 + (-5)$ f $-2 - (-1)$ g $-6 - (-4)$ h $-5 + (-4)$

2 Write true or false for each statement below.

a $7 + (-5) = -2$ b $-3 - (-4) = -7$ c $-4 - (-1) = -3$

d $-4 + (-3) = -7$ e $5 - (-4) = 1$ f $2 + (-6) = -4$

3 Copy and complete this number square.

+	−4				
−2			−8		
		−1		−6	
			3	6	
		1			6
		−5			

4 Work out $-6 + (-3) - (-5) - 4 + (-2)$

5 Vanya subtracts -3 from -7 and gets -10. Is he correct? Explain your answer fully.

6 Work out

a $-7 - (-3)$ b $4 + (-2)$ c $-9 + (-2)$ d $-5 - (-6)$

e $14 + (-8)$ f $7 - (-3)$ g $-1 + (-4)$ h $-6 - (-5)$

HWK 4M ────────────────────────────────── **Main Book page 65**

Work out

1 a $7 \times (-4)$ b $3 \times (-2)$ c -3×6 d -9×4

e $8 \times (-5)$ f -7×6 g -3×8 h $6 \times (-4)$

2 a $20 \div (-5)$ b $30 \div (-6)$ c $-10 \div 2$ d $-24 \div 3$

e $-36 \div (-4)$ f $-40 \div (-8)$ g $16 \div (-4)$ h $-50 \div (-10)$

3 Copy this number chain and fill in the empty boxes.

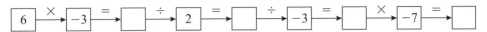

4 Work out

a $(-5)^2$ **b** $(-4) \times (-2) \times (-6)$ **c** $6 \times (-4) \times (-1)$

d $(-4)^2$ **e** $(-3) \times 4 \times 7$ **f** $(-2)^3$

5 Copy this number chain and fill in the empty boxes.

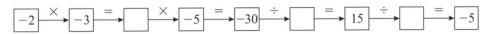

6 In golf an 'eagle' is -2, a 'birdie' is -1, par is 0 and a 'bogey' is $+1$.
During a round of golf, Jordan gets 2 eagles, 6 birdies, 8 pars and 2 bogeys.
Add up the scores to give his final total.

7 Copy and complete each empty box.

a $16 \div \square = -2$ **b** $-24 \div \square = 3$ **c** $-4 \times \square = 32$ **d** $7 \times \square = -35$

e $30 \div \square = -3$ **f** $\square \div 7 = -6$ **g** $\square \times -9 = -54$ **h** $-63 \div \square = 9$

8 If $y = mx + c$, find the value of y if $m = 3$, $x = -6$ and $c = 5$.

UNIT 2

2.1 Fractions

1   Find the missing number to make these fractions equivalent.

a $\dfrac{7}{10} = \dfrac{\square}{20}$ **b** $\dfrac{2}{5} = \dfrac{\square}{40}$ **c** $\dfrac{5}{8} = \dfrac{\square}{24}$ **d** $\dfrac{1}{7} = \dfrac{\square}{35}$

e $\dfrac{8}{9} = \dfrac{24}{\square}$ **f** $\dfrac{3}{8} = \dfrac{27}{\square}$ **g** $\dfrac{5}{6} = \dfrac{\square}{48}$ **h** $\dfrac{2}{11} = \dfrac{8}{\square}$

i $\dfrac{7}{20} = \dfrac{21}{\square}$ **j** $\dfrac{9}{100} = \dfrac{36}{\square}$ **k** $\dfrac{16}{25} = \dfrac{\square}{75}$ **l** $\dfrac{7}{15} = \dfrac{\square}{75}$

2   Cancel down each fraction to its simplest terms.

a $\dfrac{8}{20}$ **b** $\dfrac{16}{24}$ **c** $\dfrac{9}{21}$ **d** $\dfrac{12}{20}$ **e** $\dfrac{6}{18}$

f $\dfrac{32}{40}$ **g** $\dfrac{35}{45}$ **h** $\dfrac{12}{38}$ **i** $\dfrac{48}{64}$ **j** $\dfrac{75}{125}$

3   Write down which fractions are equal to $\dfrac{2}{3}$.

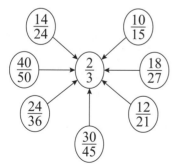

4   Is $\dfrac{15}{18}$ equivalent to $\dfrac{25}{30}$? Explain your answer clearly.

5   Write down five fractions that are equivalent to $\dfrac{5}{8}$.

6 Look at the four fractions opposite.
Change each fraction so that the
denominator is 60 and the fraction
is equivalent. Write down the fractions
in order of size, starting with the
smallest.

$\dfrac{7}{10}$ $\dfrac{11}{15}$

$\dfrac{13}{20}$ $\dfrac{3}{5}$

HWK 2M ———————————————— **Main Book page 81**

1 Copy and find the missing numbers to make these fractions equivalent.

a $\dfrac{7}{12} = \dfrac{\square}{24} = \dfrac{21}{\square}$

b $\dfrac{7}{9} = \dfrac{\square}{54} = \dfrac{49}{\square}$

c $\dfrac{\square}{3} = \dfrac{6}{18} = \dfrac{\square}{15}$

d $\dfrac{3}{24} = \dfrac{\square}{32} = \dfrac{\square}{8}$

2

A	D	E	F	H	I	K	M	N	O	R	S	V	W	Y
$\dfrac{1}{3}$	$\dfrac{2}{5}$	$\dfrac{5}{9}$	$\dfrac{4}{5}$	$\dfrac{3}{7}$	$\dfrac{5}{12}$	$\dfrac{1}{6}$	$\dfrac{3}{8}$	$\dfrac{1}{4}$	$\dfrac{5}{6}$	$\dfrac{11}{20}$	$\dfrac{3}{4}$	$\dfrac{1}{8}$	$\dfrac{7}{10}$	$\dfrac{4}{9}$

Cancel each fraction below and select the letter from the table above to make a sentence.

$\dfrac{15}{36}$ $\dfrac{18}{42}$ — $\dfrac{7}{21}$ $\dfrac{4}{32}$ $\dfrac{40}{72}$ — $\dfrac{12}{15}$ $\dfrac{20}{48}$ $\dfrac{9}{36}$ $\dfrac{45}{108}$ $\dfrac{24}{32}$ $\dfrac{9}{21}$ $\dfrac{35}{63}$ $\dfrac{20}{50}$

$\dfrac{36}{96}$ $\dfrac{60}{135}$ — $\dfrac{24}{56}$ $\dfrac{30}{36}$ $\dfrac{60}{160}$ $\dfrac{25}{45}$ $\dfrac{28}{40}$ $\dfrac{55}{66}$ $\dfrac{77}{140}$ $\dfrac{16}{96}$

HWK 3M ———————————————— **Main Book page 82**

1 Work out

a $\dfrac{1}{4}$ of £36

b $\dfrac{1}{7}$ of 63 cm

c $\dfrac{1}{6}$ of 54 kg

d $\dfrac{1}{12}$ of 240 kg

e $\dfrac{1}{9}$ of £45

f $\dfrac{1}{20}$ of 300 g

g $\dfrac{1}{50}$ of 600 cm

h $\dfrac{1}{100}$ of £8000

i $\dfrac{1}{8}$ of 200 kg

2 Find each missing number

a $\dfrac{1}{\square}$ of 42 = 7

b $\dfrac{1}{\square}$ of 49 = 7

c $\dfrac{1}{\square}$ of 400 = 40

d $\dfrac{1}{\square}$ of 120 = 6

e $\dfrac{1}{\square}$ of 75 = 25

f $\dfrac{1}{\square}$ of 180 = 6

3 Charlie has 56 marbles. He loses $\frac{1}{8}$ of the marbles.

   a How many marbles does he lose?

   b How many marbles does he have left?

4 Donna has a snake which is 180 cm long. 3 months later the snake has grown by $\frac{1}{10}$. How long is the snake now?

5 Work out

   a $\frac{1}{6}$ of 24　　　**b** $\frac{5}{6}$ of 24　　　**c** $\frac{2}{5}$ of 20　　　**d** $\frac{3}{4}$ of 28

   e $\frac{5}{8}$ of 48　　　**f** $\frac{4}{9}$ of 54　　　**g** $\frac{2}{7}$ of 21　　　**h** $\frac{9}{10}$ of 160

6 Carol brings £8 to school and spends $\frac{3}{4}$ of this money. How much money does she have left?

7 There are 140 pupils in Year 7. If $\frac{3}{7}$ of the pupils are boys, how many girls are there?

HWK 3E ——————————————————————————— **Main Book page 83**

1 Work out

   a $\frac{4}{7}$ of 350 kg　　　**b** $\frac{5}{6}$ of 72 cm　　　**c** $\frac{7}{9}$ of £135

   d $\frac{3}{8}$ of £176　　　**e** $\frac{7}{12}$ of 84 litres　　　**f** $\frac{9}{20}$ of 2600 kg

   g $\frac{4}{15}$ of 240 g　　　**h** $\frac{7}{11}$ of £132　　　**i** $\frac{13}{25}$ of £225

2 234 people watch a film at the cinema. $\frac{5}{9}$ of these people are children. How many of these people are *not* children?

3 Jasmine earns £1560 each month. She uses $\frac{3}{8}$ of the money to pay her rent and $\frac{2}{5}$ of the money for her food and bills. How much money does she have left over each month?

4 Which is larger ($\frac{6}{7}$ of 189) or ($\frac{4}{9}$ of 369) and by how much?

5 Ashley has £160. She takes $\frac{4}{5}$ of this money into town and spends $\frac{3}{8}$ of it on a meal. How much did the meal cost?

6 Find each missing number below.

a $\frac{7}{\square}$ of 56 = 49

b $\frac{5}{\square}$ of 72 = 45

c $\frac{\square}{7}$ of 21 = 9

d $\frac{10}{\square}$ of 88 = 80

e $\frac{7}{\square}$ of 54 = 42

f $\frac{2}{\square}$ of 63 = 18

7 $\frac{3}{8}$ of a number is 9. What is the number?

HWK 4M ————————————————————————— **Main Book page 85**

1 Remember that $\frac{3}{4} \times \frac{5}{7} = \frac{3 \times 5}{4 \times 7} = \frac{15}{28}$

Work out

a $\frac{5}{6} \times \frac{1}{3}$

b $\frac{3}{7} \times \frac{2}{5}$

c $\frac{1}{3}$ of $\frac{1}{5}$

d $\frac{4}{5} \times \frac{10}{11}$

e $\frac{1}{4} \times \frac{8}{9}$

f $\frac{1}{6}$ of $\frac{3}{8}$

g $\frac{4}{5} \times \frac{5}{8}$

h $\frac{4}{7} \times \frac{14}{15}$

Make sure you have cancelled all the above answers whenever possible.

2 Work out the area of this rectangle.

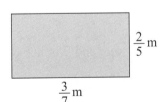

$\frac{2}{5}$ m

$\frac{3}{7}$ m

3 Remember that $\frac{7}{1}$ means $7 \div 1$, which equals 7, so $7 = \frac{7}{1}$

Work out

a $\frac{2}{3} \times \frac{30}{1}$

b $\frac{3}{5} \times 40$

c $\frac{5}{8} \times 24$

d $\frac{5}{9} \times 63$

e $\frac{6}{7} \times 42$

f $\frac{7}{20} \times 180$

g $\frac{8}{11} \times 121$

h $\frac{5}{6} \times 48$

4 A bottle contains $\frac{7}{10}$ of a litre of water. Aidan drinks $\frac{4}{5}$ of this water. How much water is left in the bottle?

5 Work out $\dfrac{1}{4} \times \dfrac{3}{5} \times \dfrac{6}{7}$

6 Work out $\dfrac{5}{8} \times \dfrac{2}{3} \times 60$

7 If $\dfrac{3}{8} \times n = \dfrac{27}{88}$, write down the value of n as a fraction.

HWK 5M	Main Book page 87

Copy and complete

1 $\dfrac{1}{5} + \dfrac{2}{5} = \dfrac{\square}{5}$

2 $\dfrac{1}{4} + \dfrac{3}{8} = \dfrac{\square}{8} + \dfrac{3}{8} = \dfrac{\square}{8}$

Work out

3 $\dfrac{6}{7} - \dfrac{2}{7}$

4 $\dfrac{5}{9} + \dfrac{2}{9}$

5 $\dfrac{7}{8} - \dfrac{1}{4}$

6 $\dfrac{7}{20} - \dfrac{1}{5}$

7 $\dfrac{3}{16} + \dfrac{3}{4}$

8 $\dfrac{5}{18} + \dfrac{1}{6}$

9 $\dfrac{13}{20} - \dfrac{1}{2}$

10 $\dfrac{7}{25} + \dfrac{3}{5}$

11 Mark used $\dfrac{1}{4}$ kg of mixed fruit and $\dfrac{1}{8}$ kg of sugar when making a cake. How much mixed fruit and sugar did he use in total?

12 Cindy gave $\dfrac{3}{10}$ of her sweets to her brother and $\dfrac{2}{5}$ of her sweets to her sister. What total fraction of her sweets did she give away?

13 Copy and use the square to explain why $\dfrac{1}{2} + \dfrac{1}{4}$ does not equal $\dfrac{1+1}{2+4} = \dfrac{2}{6} = \dfrac{1}{3}$

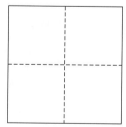

14 After a festival, Aaron and Mary clear up some of their rubbish. Aaron takes $\dfrac{7}{12}$ of the rubbish and Mary takes $\dfrac{1}{3}$ of the rubbish. What fraction of their rubbish has not been cleared?

HWK 6M ──────────────────────── **Main Book page 88**

1 Copy and complete each box below.

a $\dfrac{1}{3} + \dfrac{1}{4}$

$= \dfrac{\square}{12} + \dfrac{\square}{12}$

$= \dfrac{\square}{12}$

b $\dfrac{3}{5} - \dfrac{1}{4}$

$= \dfrac{\square}{20} - \dfrac{\square}{20}$

$= \dfrac{\square}{20}$

c $\dfrac{9}{10} - \dfrac{3}{7}$

$= \dfrac{\square}{70} - \dfrac{\square}{70}$

$= \dfrac{\square}{70}$

In questions **2** to **13** , work out the answers and cancel if necessary.

2 $\dfrac{1}{3} + \dfrac{2}{5}$

3 $\dfrac{1}{4} + \dfrac{1}{7}$

4 $\dfrac{3}{4} - \dfrac{1}{3}$

5 $\dfrac{5}{6} - \dfrac{2}{5}$

6 $\dfrac{2}{9} + \dfrac{3}{7}$

7 $\dfrac{7}{11} - \dfrac{5}{9}$

8 $\dfrac{7}{8} - \dfrac{4}{5}$

9 $\dfrac{1}{6} + \dfrac{3}{10}$

10 $\dfrac{7}{20} - \dfrac{1}{9}$

11 $\dfrac{9}{16} + \dfrac{2}{5}$

12 $\dfrac{2}{5} - \dfrac{3}{20}$

13 $\dfrac{9}{10} - \dfrac{4}{7}$

14 In a class $\dfrac{1}{10}$ of the children cycle to school, $\dfrac{1}{3}$ of the children walk, $\dfrac{1}{5}$ come by car and the rest come by bus.

    a What total fraction of the children cycle, walk or come by car?

    b What fraction of the class comes by bus?

15

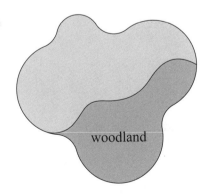
woodland

$\dfrac{4}{9}$ of a park is woodland.

Another $\dfrac{1}{5}$ of the park is to be turned into woodland.

What fraction of the park will now be woodland?

16 Find the missing fraction for each box. Cancel if necessary.

    a $\dfrac{1}{4} + \square = \dfrac{7}{12}$

    b $\dfrac{3}{5} - \square = \dfrac{1}{10}$

    c $\dfrac{5}{6} - \square = \dfrac{11}{24}$

17 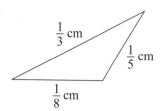 Find the perimeter of this triangle.

$\frac{1}{3}$ cm

$\frac{1}{5}$ cm

$\frac{1}{8}$ cm

18 A farmer uses $\frac{1}{4}$ of his farm for cereals, $\frac{1}{5}$ for cattle, $\frac{7}{30}$ for sheep and the rest is left unused. What fraction is unused?

19 Richard read $\frac{3}{8}$ of his book one day and $\frac{2}{5}$ the next day. What fraction of the book remains to be read?

2.2 Fractions, decimals, percentages

HWK 1M   **Main Book page 92**

1 Write these fractions as decimals.

    a $\frac{3}{10}$ **b** $\frac{17}{100}$ **c** $\frac{1}{4}$ **d** $\frac{43}{100}$ **e** $\frac{1}{10}$

2 Remember: $\dfrac{7}{25} = \dfrac{28}{100} = 0.28$

Write these fractions as decimals.

    a $\frac{3}{25}$ **b** $\frac{19}{20}$ **c** $\frac{4}{5}$ **d** $\frac{180}{200}$ **e** $\frac{12}{16}$

    f $\frac{13}{20}$ **g** $\frac{150}{300}$ **h** $\frac{19}{25}$ **i** $\frac{12}{40}$ **j** $\frac{11}{20}$

3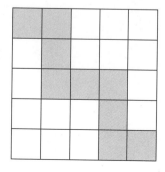

    a What fraction of this diagram is shaded?

    b Write this fraction as a decimal.

4 Eli says 0.5 is $\frac{1}{5}$. Explain clearly why Eli is not correct.

5 Write these fractions as decimals.

a $\frac{28}{40}$ b $\frac{3}{125}$ c $\frac{18}{72}$ d $\frac{19}{250}$ e $\frac{27}{36}$

f $\frac{240}{2000}$ g $\frac{63}{500}$ h $\frac{39}{125}$ i $\frac{84}{4000}$ j $\frac{64}{80}$

6 Which number is larger? $\frac{17}{20}$ or 0.9

7 Which number is larger? 0.65 or $\frac{16}{25}$

8 Copy and complete the table.

Fraction	$\frac{1}{25}$	$\frac{3}{20}$		$\frac{17}{1000}$		$\frac{19}{50}$	$\frac{13}{52}$		$\frac{45}{500}$
Decimal			0.8		0.75			0.02	

HWK 2M ——————————————————— **Main Book page 93**

1 Write these decimals as fractions.

a 0.9   b 0.03   c 0.29   d 0.5   e 0.87

f 0.63   g 0.75   h 7.9   i 3.83   j 4.17

2 Haroon has done 0.43 of his homework.

a What fraction of his homework has he done?

b What fraction of his homework has he still got to do?

3 Copy and complete

a $0.8 = \frac{\square}{10} = \frac{\square}{5}$

b $0.06 = \frac{\square}{100} = \frac{\square}{50}$

c $0.36 = \frac{\square}{100} = \frac{\square}{25}$

d $0.87 = \frac{\square}{\square}$

e $0.18 = \frac{\square}{100} = \frac{\square}{\square}$

f $0.35 = \frac{\square}{100} = \frac{\square}{\square}$

4 Melissa has eaten 0.44 of her pizza. What fraction of her pizza is left? Cancel down the answer if possible.

42

5 Write these decimals as fractions. Cancel down the fractions when possible.

a 0.6   **b** 0.08   **c** 0.28   **d** 0.45   **e** 0.34

f 0.65   **g** 0.25   **h** 0.14   **i** 0.2   **j** 0.76

k 5.4   **l** 3.24   **m** 5.85   **n** 8.75   **o** 2.16

6 Match up the creatures with the equivalent decimals and fractions.

a $\frac{14}{40}$

b $\frac{4}{25}$

c  0.84

d  $\frac{7}{50}$

e  0.95

f  $\frac{21}{25}$

g 0.14

h  $\frac{19}{20}$

i  0.16

j 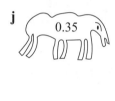 0.35

HWK 3M   **Main Book page 94**

1 $80\% = \frac{80}{100} = \frac{4}{5}$ Change these percentages into fractions.

a 90%   **b** 46%   **c** 13%   **d** 6%   **e** 45%

2 Copy and complete the following.

a $\frac{7}{20} = \frac{35}{100} = \boxed{}\%$ **b** $\frac{17}{50} = \frac{\boxed{}}{100} = \boxed{}\%$

$\frac{\boxed{}}{100} = \boxed{}\%$ **d** $\frac{12}{25} = \frac{\boxed{}}{100} = \boxed{}\%$

red $\frac{16}{25}$ and Gary scored 65%. Who got the higher mark?

4 Tim is collecting football cards. He has collected $\frac{11}{20}$ of the cards. What percentage of the cards does he still need to collect?

5 Change each fraction below into a percentage then write out the fractions in order of size, starting with the smallest.

$\frac{9}{20}$ $\frac{1}{2}$ $\frac{9}{25}$ $\frac{23}{50}$ $\frac{1}{3}$ $\frac{2}{5}$ $\frac{3}{10}$

6 Answer true or false for each of the following statements.

a $8\% = 0.8$ **b** $\frac{3}{50} > 5\%$ **c** $40\% > \frac{7}{20}$

7 $\frac{3}{10}$ of a group of children go swimming and $\frac{7}{25}$ of the group of children go ice skating. What percentage of the children do *not* swim or ice skate?

HWK 4M ──────────────────────────────── **Main Book page 95**

1 Write these percentages as decimals.

a 39%   **b** 38%   **c** 20%   **d** 29%   **e** 140%   **f** 375%

2 Copy and complete the following.

a $0.61 = \dfrac{\square}{100} = \square\%$ **b** $0.6 = \dfrac{6}{10} = \dfrac{\square}{100} = \square\%$

c $0.09 = \dfrac{\square}{100} = \square\%$ **d** $0.16 = \dfrac{\square}{100} = \square\%$

3 Draw a 10 × 10 square. Use this diagram to explain why 0.4 is equal to 40% and not 4%.

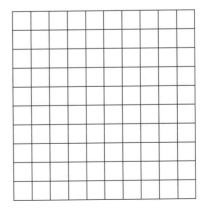

4 Mary, Lee and Todd are trying to lose weight. One week Mary loses 0.3 kg, Lee loses $\frac{8}{25}$ kg and Todd loses 31% of a kilogram. Who loses the most weight?

5 At a wedding, 74% of the wedding cake is eaten. 0.12 of the cake is kept to celebrate the first born baby. The rest of the cake is given to the bride's mother. What fraction of the cake is given to the bride's mother?

6 Answer true or false for each of the following statements.

a $\frac{7}{50} = 14\%$　　　**b** $\frac{4}{25} = 16\%$　　　**c** $\frac{1}{3} = 35\%$

7 Cooper scores 12 marks out of 20. He says that he has scored a higher mark than his friend, Leo. Is this true if Leo scored 58%? Give full reasons for your answer.

8 Copy and complete the table.

Fraction	$\frac{13}{25}$					$\frac{13}{20}$	$\frac{9}{50}$	
Decimal			0.19	0.24				
Percentage		15%			26%			92%

2.3 Coordinates

HWK 1M ———————————————————————————————— **Main Book page 101**

1 On this grid each square represents 1 m by 1 m.
Write down the coordinates of:

a Tom

b the dog.

c Tom may only travel along the lines.
He travels 3 m to the dog. How many
different ways might he have gone?

Write down the coordinates of:

d Ken

e Ali

f the cat.

g Ali may only travel along the lines.
She travels 4 m to the cat. How many
different ways might she have gone?

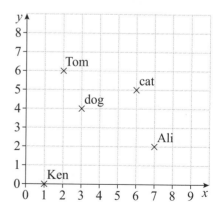

For questions **2** and **3**, plot the points given and join them up in order.

Write down what the picture is.

2

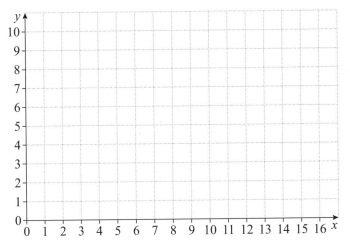

a (12, 2), (13, 2), (12, 4)

b (6, 2), (7, 2), (7, 5), (11, 4), (11, 1), (12, 1), (12, 4) (13, $5\frac{1}{2}$), ($15\frac{1}{2}$, $5\frac{1}{2}$), ($15\frac{1}{2}$, 8), (15, 8), (15, 6), (13, 6), (12, 7), (6, 8), (6, 9), (5, 10), (5, 9), (2, 8), (2, 7), (3, 7), (2, 6), (5, 7), (5, 1), (6, 1), (6, 4), (7, 5)

c Draw a dot at (4, 8).

3

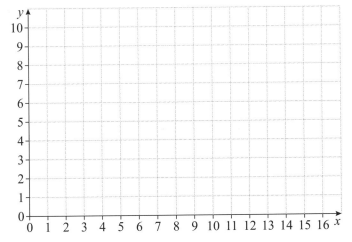

a (5, 5), (5, 6), (11, 6), (11, 5)

b (7, 6), (7, 7), (8, 7), (8, 6)

c ($5\frac{1}{2}$, 7), ($5\frac{1}{2}$, 8), (4, 8), (4, 9)

d (5, 6), (5, 7), (6, 7), (6, 6)

e ($7\frac{1}{2}$, 7), ($7\frac{1}{2}$, 8), (6, 8), (6, 9)

f (12, 4), (2, 4), (3, 2), (12, 2), (14, 4), (12, 4), (12, 5), (4, 5), (4, 4)

g Draw dots at (5, $4\frac{1}{2}$), (6, $4\frac{1}{2}$), (7, $4\frac{1}{2}$), (8, $4\frac{1}{2}$), (9, $4\frac{1}{2}$), (10, $4\frac{1}{2}$), (11, $4\frac{1}{2}$), (6, $5\frac{1}{2}$), (7, $5\frac{1}{2}$), (8, $5\frac{1}{2}$), (9, $5\frac{1}{2}$), (10, $5\frac{1}{2}$).

The letters from A to Z are shown on the grid.
Coded messages can be sent using coordinates.

For example, $(-4, -2)\,(-4, 2)\,(-4, 2)\,(4, 2)$
reads 'FOOD'.

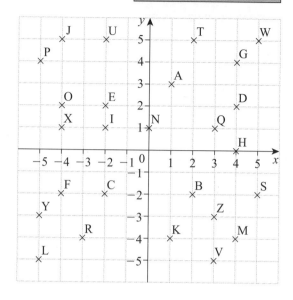

Decipher the following messages.

1 $(5, 5)\,(4, 0)\,(1, 3)\,(2, 5)\,\#\,(4, 2)\,(-4, 2)\,\#\,(-5, -3)$
$(-4, 2)\,(-2, 5)\,\#\,(-2, -2)\,(1, 3)\,(-5, -5)\,(-5, -5)\,\#$
$(1, 3)\,\#\,(4, -4)\,(1, 3)\,(0, 1)\,\#\,(5, 5)\,(-2, 1)\,(2, 5)\,(4, 0)\,\#$
$(1, 3)\,\#\,(5, -2)\,(-5, 4)\,(1, 3)\,(4, 2)\,(-2, 2)\,\#\,(-4, 2)$
$(0, 1)\,\#\,(4, 0)\,(-2, 1)\,(5, -2)\,\#\,(4, 0)\,(-2, 2)\,(1, 3)$
$(4, 2)?\,(4, 2)\,(-4, 2)\,(-2, 5)\,(4, 4)!$

2 $(5, 5)\,(4, 0)\,(1, 3)\,(2, 5)\,\#\,(4, 2)\,(-4, 2)\,\#\,(-5, -3)$
$(-4, 2)\,(-2, 5)\,\#\,(-2, -2)\,(1, 3)\,(-5, -5)\,(-5, -5)\,\#$
$(1, 3)\,\#\,(4, 2)\,(-2, 2)\,(1, 3)\,(4, 2)\,\#\,(-5, 4)\,(1, 3)\,(-3, -4)$
$(-3, -4)\,(-4, 2)\,(2, 5)?\,(-5, 4)\,(-4, 2)\,(-5, -5)\,(-5, -3)$
$(4, 4)\,(-4, 2)\,(0, 1)!$

3 $(5, 5)\,(-2, 1)\,(2, 5)\,(4, 0)\,\#\,(5, 5)\,(4, 0)\,(1, 3)\,(2, 5)\,\#$
$(4, 2)\,(-4, 2)\,\#\,(-5, -3)\,(-4, 2)\,(-2, 5)\,\#\,(5, -2)\,(2, 5)$
$(-2, 5)\,(-4, -2)\,(-4, -2)\,\#\,(1, 3)\,\#\,(4, 2)\,(-2, 2)\,(1, 3)$
$(4, 2)\,\#\,(-5, 4)\,(1, 3)\,(-3, -4)\,(-3, -4)\,(-4, 2)$
$(2, 5)\,?\,(-5, 4)\,(-4, 2)\,(-5, -5)\,(-5, -3)\,(-4, -2)\,(-2, 1)$
$(-5, -5)\,(-5, -5)\,(1, 3)!$

4 Write a message or joke of your own using coordinates. Ask a friend to decipher your words
at the start of your next lesson.

1 Draw axes from 0 to 5. Plot the three points given and then find the coordinates of the point which makes a rectangle when the points are joined up.

(1, 2)　　　(1, 4)　　　(5, 4)

2 Write down the coordinates of the fourth vertex (corner) of this square.

3 **a** Draw axes from 0 to 5. Plot the three points given and then find the coordinates of the point which makes a square when the points are joined up.

(5, 4)　　　(2, 4)　　　(2, 1)

b Write down the coordinates of the centre of the square.

4 **a** Copy and complete this parallelogram.

b Join the opposite vertices (corners) together and write down the coordinates of the point where these two lines meet.

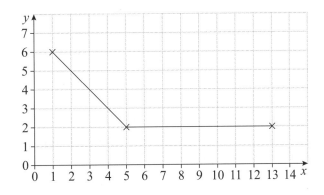

5 **a** T, R and S are three corners of a square. Write down the coordinates of the other corner.

b R, S and U are three corners of a rectangle. Write down the coordinates of the other corner.

c P, Q and R are three corners of another square. Write down the coordinates of the other corner. (Draw the diagram if you need to.)

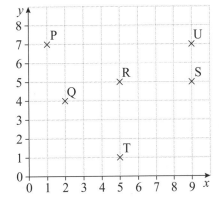

48

2.4 Straight line graphs

1

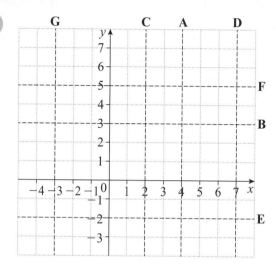

The equation of line A is $x = 4$

The equation of line B is $y = 3$

Write down the equations of the lines C, D, E, F and G.

2 Draw x and y axes from 0 to 6.
Draw the lines $x = 5$ and $y = 1$ and write down the coordinates of the point where the two lines meet.

3 Draw x and y axes from 0 to 6.
Plot and label the points P(2, 1), Q(4, 4), R(6, 2), S(5, 2), T(6, 4), U(2, 6) and V(2, 4).
R and S lie on the line $y = 2$.

   a List the points on the line $y = 4$.

   b Write down the equation of the line passing through R and T.

   c List the points on the line $x = 2$.

   d Write down the points on the line $x = 5$.

4

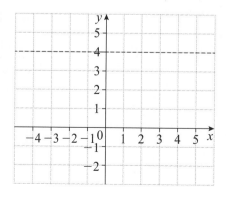

The broken line is moved 5 units downwards parallel to the y-axis. Write down the equation of this line in its new position.

1 For each graph write down the coordinates of the points marked and find the equation of the line through the points.

a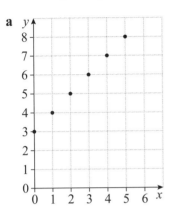

b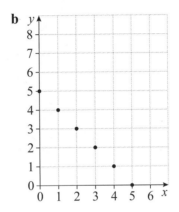

2 Write down the equation of the line which passes through the points (1, 2), (2, 4), (3, 6), (4, 8) and (5, 10).

3

x	y
10	4
11	5
12	6
13	7

This table shows some points on a line.
Find the equation of the line.

4 A line passes through (0, m), (1, 6), (2, 7), (3, 8), (4, 9) and (5, n).

a Write down the equation of the line through the points.

b Write down the values of m and n.

5 Julian says that the equation of the line through the points opposite is $y = x + 6$.
Explain clearly the mistake that Julian has made.

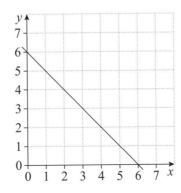

50

6 Find the equation for
  a line A
  b line B
  c line C
  d line D
  e line E

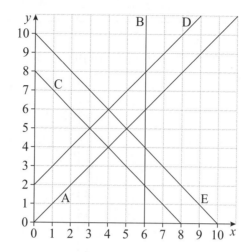

1 For the line $y = x - 5$, find the y values for
  a $x = 8$ **b** $x = 10$ **c** $x = 11$

2 For the line $y = 6x$, find the y values for
  a $x = 3$ **b** $x = 7$ **c** $x = 12$

3 Does the point $(2, 6)$ lie on the line $y = x + 4$?

4 Does the point $(3, 12)$ lie on the line $y = 4x$ or on the line $y = 9x$?

5

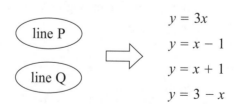

$$y = 3x$$
$$y = x - 1$$
$$y = x + 1$$
$$y = 3 - x$$

Match up line P and line Q to the correct equation.

6 Which points below lie on the line $y = 7 - x$?

    A $(2, 9)$ B $(3, 4)$ C $(1, 6)$ D $(3, 10)$

7   **a** The equation of a line is $y = x + 2$. Copy and complete this list of points on the line.

         $(0, 2), (1, \Box), (2, \Box), (3, \Box), (4, \Box)$

   b Draw x and y axes from 0 to 6.

   c Plot the points and join them up to draw the graph of $y = x + 2$.

In questions **8** and **9** you are given the equation of a line and a list of points on the line.

Fill in the missing numbers, draw x and y axes and then draw the graph.

8 $y = 5 - x; (0, \Box) (1, \Box) (2, \Box) (3, \Box)$

9 $y = 2x - 1; (1, 1) (2, \Box) (3, \Box) (4, \Box) (5, \Box)$

2.5 Perimeter and area

HWK 1M   **Main Book page 118**

1   **a** Which shape below has the larger perimeter – the square with sides 13 cm or the rectangle measuring 17.5 cm by 7.5 cm?

     13 cm   7.5 cm

                                 17.5 cm

   b Write down the difference between the perimeters of the square and rectangle above.

2 The perimeter of a rectangular swimming pool is 74 m. What is the length of the pool if the width is 12 m?

3 A rectangular picture has a perimeter of 228 cm. How long is the shorter side if the longer side is 78 cm?

4 Find the perimeter of each shape. The lengths are in cm.

a

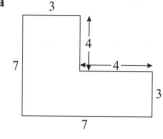

b

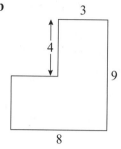

c

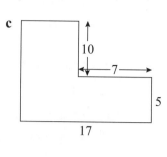

d

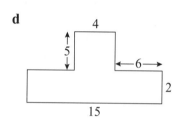

e

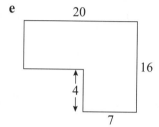

f

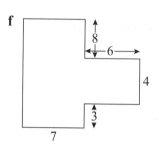

5

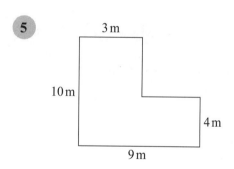

This is a plan of Neil's room. He wants to put coving around the perimeter of his room. The coving comes in 4 m pieces. How many pieces of coving must Neil buy?

6

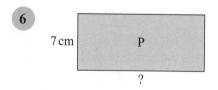

The perimeter of rectangle P is equal to the perimeter of square Q. Write down the missing length of rectangle P.

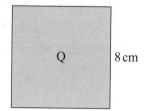

1　　**a** Find the area of square A and square B.

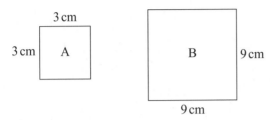

　　b How many square A's would fit into square B exactly?

2　　What is the area of this lawn?

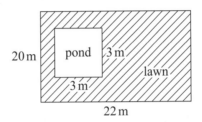

3　　A rectangle has an area of 56 cm². If the length is 8 cm, what is the width?

4　　A rectangle has an area of 75 m². If the length is 10 m, what is the width?

5　　Find the area of each shape. The lengths are in cm.

a

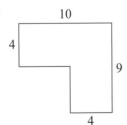

b

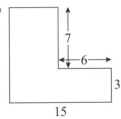

c

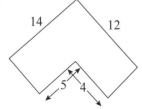

d

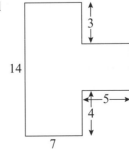

6 **a** How long is each side of this square?

b What is the perimeter of this square?

7 Work out the shaded area opposite. The lengths are in cm.

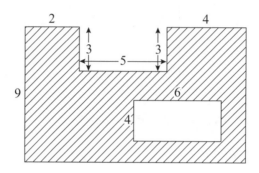

8

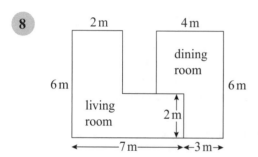

Shannon wants to carpet her living room and dining room. What is the total area of carpet she will need?

HWK 3M ——————————————————————— **Main Book page 122**

1 Find the area of each shape.

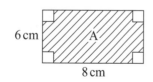

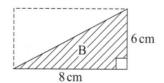

2 Find the area of each triangle. The lengths are in cm.

a    **b** 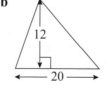   **c** 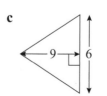   **d**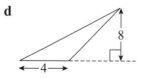

3

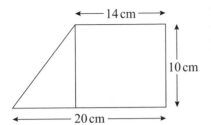

These two shapes have the same area.
Find the value of *x*.

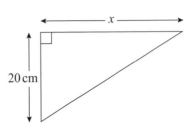

4 Find the total area of each shape. The lengths are in cm.

a

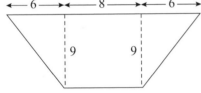

b

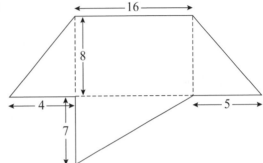

5

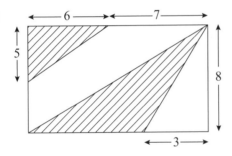

Find the total shaded area. The lengths are in cm.

6 Denise is painting both ends of her house.
Each pot of paint will cover 15 m².
How many pots of paint will Denise need?

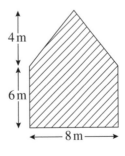

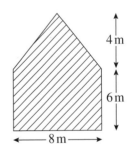

7

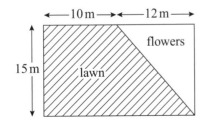

Calculate the area of the lawn.

8 This diagram shows a room with a rug 4 m by 4 m.

    a What is the total area of the room?

    b What is the area of the rug?

    c What area of the floor is *not* covered by the rug?

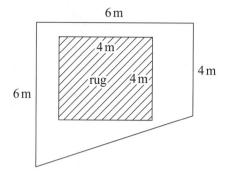

2.6 Angles

HWK 1M ————————————————————— **Main Book page 128**

In questions **1** and **2**, use uppercase letters to indicate the angles shown by the lowercase letters in italics (for example: $a = R\hat{Q}T$).

1

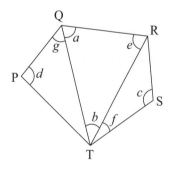

2

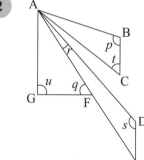

3 Melissa says that $A\hat{B}C = 113°$.
Explain why you think she
has decided on this answer.

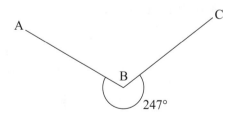

4 Use the diagram to give the value of each angle.

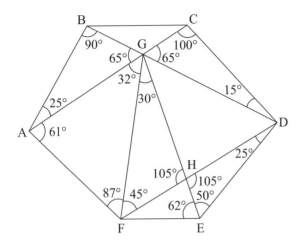

a AĜF   b FĜE

c AĜB   d BĜF

e DĤE   f BÂF

g AF̂G   h AĜH

i AF̂H   j DĈG

k BĜE   l DÊF

HWK 2M/3M ──────────────── **Main Book page 129**

1

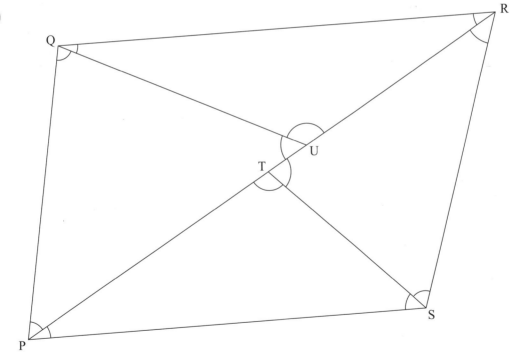

Use a protractor to measure these angles on the diagram above.

a PÛQ   b TR̂S   c RÛU   d QP̂U   e PŜR   f RT̂S

g QR̂S   h SP̂T   i RŜT   j PT̂S   k PQ̂R   l PŜT

58

2 Use a protractor to draw the following angles accurately.

a

70°

b

140°

c

125°

d 35°   **e** 115°   **f** 58°   **g** 27°   **h** 132°   **i** 163°

3 Use a ruler and protractor to draw the diagram opposite. Measure AĈB.

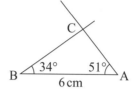

B   34°   51° A
    6 cm

4 Write down whether an angle of 168° is acute, obtuse or reflex.

5 Write a sentence to explain how large an obtuse angle is.

HWK 4M ──────────────────────────────── **Main Book page 132**

Find the angles marked with letters.

1

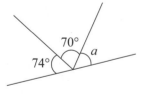

70°
74°   a

2

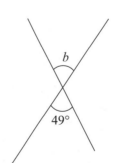

b

49°

3

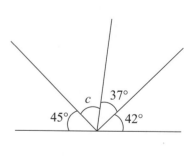

c   37°
45°   42°

4

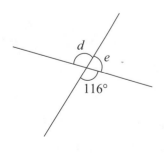

d   e
116°

5

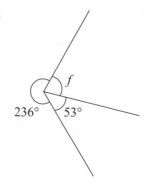

f
236°   53°

6

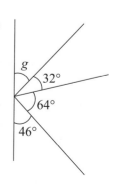

g   32°
64°
46°

59

7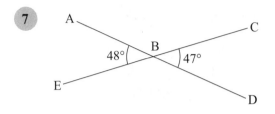

AD and CE are straight lines.
Ossie measures AB̂E and CB̂D
and writes his answers on the
diagram as shown.
Explain why Ossie cannot be correct.

In questions **8** to **13** find the angles marked with letters.

8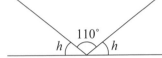

9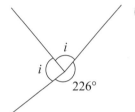

10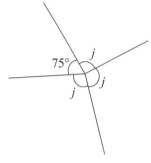

11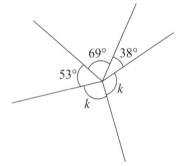

12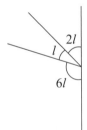

13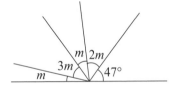

14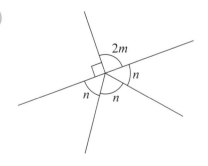

Explain clearly why $m = 45°$
and $n = 60°$.

Find the angles marked with letters.

1
62° 49°
a

2
b
28°

3
47°
86°
c

4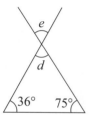
e
d
36° 75°

5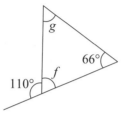
g
66°
110° f

6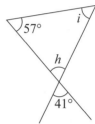
57° i
h
41°

7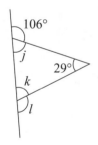
106°
j
29°
k
l

8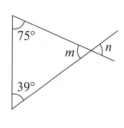
75°
m n
39°

9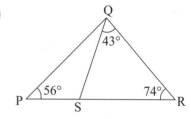

Find the value of PQ̂S

10 Use the diagram opposite to prove that

AB̂C + BÂC = BĈD

Give full reasons in your proof.

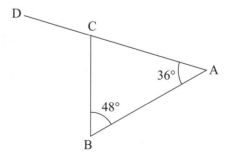

Find the angles marked with letters.

1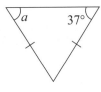

2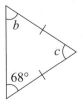

3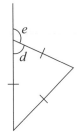

4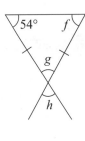

5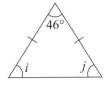

6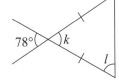

7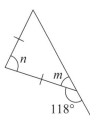

8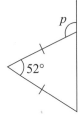

9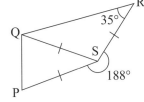

Find the value of QP̂S.

10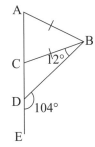

Find the value of AB̂C.

Explain clearly why
DĈE is equal to 60°.

11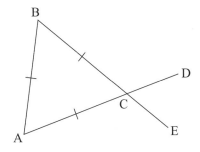

12 One of the angles in an isosceles triangle is 30°. Agnes says that the two other angles must be 30° and 120°. Jay says that Agnes is *not definitely* correct. *Explain clearly* why Jay says this.

HWK 7M ── **Main Book page 138**

1 Work out the values of EB̂C and HĈB, giving reasons for your answers.

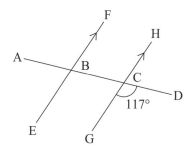

In questions **2** to **9**, find the angles marked with letters.

2

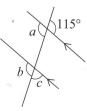

3

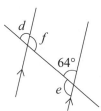

4

5

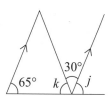

6

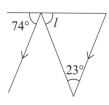

7

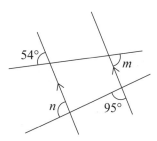

8

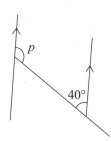

9

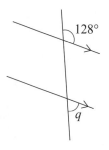

10

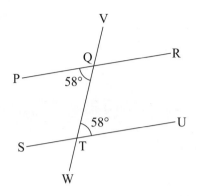

Give a reason why we know that lines PR and SU are parallel.

UNIT 3

3.1 Properties of numbers

1   Write down all the prime numbers shown below.

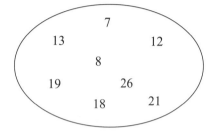

2   When two prime numbers are added the answer is 18. What could the two numbers be?

3   The difference between two prime numbers is another prime number. Write down three sets of numbers where this would be true.

4   Write down all the prime numbers between 30 and 40.

5   Find four prime numbers which add up to another prime number.

6   Is 89 a prime number?

7   **a** List all the prime numbers between 100 and 110.
       b *Explain* what you did to check that these numbers were prime.

8   *Explain* why only one even number is a prime number.

1   1, 2, 3, 6 and 18 are factors of 18. Write down the one remaining factor.

2   Write down all the factors of 28. There are six factors.

3   Which numbers below are *not* multiples of 15?

| 30 | | 70 | | 60 | | 90 | | 80 | | 45 |

4   Which numbers below are multiples of 7?

| 28 | 63 | 36 | 82 | 84 | 54 |

5   Find three numbers that are multiples of both 4 and 5.

6   The factors of a number are 1, 5 and 25. What is the number?

7   Write down all the *odd* factors of 24.

8   Find two numbers that are multiples of 3, 4 and 8.

9   Which of these numbers is *not* a multiple of 21?

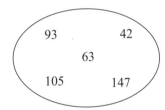

93   42
    63
105   147

10   Write down all the factors of
a 7   **b** 13   **c** 5   **d** 17

11   Look at your answers to question **9**. How many factors do prime numbers have?

12   How many numbers less than 10 have exactly two factors?

HWK 3M ───────────────────────────────── **Main Book page 162**

1   Here is a factor tree for 45.

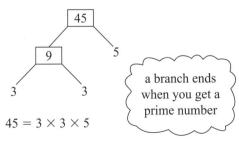

45 = 3 × 3 × 5

a branch ends when you get a prime number

a Draw a factor tree for 40.

b Copy and complete
40 = ? × ? × ? × ?

2   **a** Draw a factor tree for 48.

b Copy and complete 48 = ? × ? × ? × ? × ?

3 Draw a factor tree for each number below and write each number as a product of its prime factors.

    a 120   **b** 300   **c** 350   **d** 65

4 Ryan draws the factor tree shown opposite so that he can write 432 as a product of its prime factors.

Explain clearly any mistakes that Ryan has made.

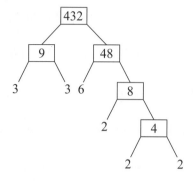

$$432 = 2 \times 2 \times 2 \times 3 \times 3 \times 6$$

5 How many different prime factors does 405 have?

HWK 4M   **Main Book page 163**

1 The factors of 18 are 1, 2, 3, 6, 9, 18.

The factors of 12 are 1, 2, 3, 4, 6, 12.

Write down the <u>H</u>ighest <u>C</u>ommon <u>F</u>actor of 18 and 12.

2   **a** List all the factors of 20.

    b List all the factors of 30.

    c Write down the H.C.F. of 20 and 30.

3 Find the H.C.F. of

    a 24 and 36   **b** 25 and 45

4 9, 18, 27, 36, 45 are multiples of 9.

12, 24, 36, 48, 60 are multiples of 12.

Write down the <u>L</u>owest <u>C</u>ommon <u>M</u>ultiple of 9 and 12.

5   **a** List the first six multiples of 6.

    b List the first six multiples of 8.

    c Write down the L.C.M. of 6 and 8.

6 Find the L.C.M. of

    a 4 and 9   **b** 12 and 15

7 Write down two numbers whose L.C.M. is 20.

8 Find the H.C.F. of 42 and 56.

9 A nurse visits Sarah's grandmother every 8 days. A doctor visits Sarah's grandmother every 7 days. The nurse and doctor both visit on 17th June. On what date do both the nurse and doctor next visit Sarah's grandmother at the same time?

10 10 is the L.C.M. of 2, 10 and n. Write down the value of n.

HWK 5M ———————————————————————— **Main Book page 164**

1 Copy and complete: $7^2 = 7 \times 7 = \boxed{}$

Work out

2 9^2

3 11^2

4 $5^2 + 3^2$

5 $10^2 - 6^2$

6 $8^2 - 6^2$

7 $6^2 + 1^2$

8 $12^2 + 8^2$

9 $20^2 - 10^2$

10 Which square number is between 30 and 40?

11 **a** Copy and complete the pattern below as far as 10×10.

$2 \times 2 = 1 \times 1 + 3$
$3 \times 3 = 2 \times 2 + 5$
$4 \times 4 = 3 \times 3 + 7$
$5 \times 5 = 4 \times 4 + \ldots$
$\vdots$
$10 \times 10 = \ldots\ldots$

b What is the result for 15×15?

c What is the result for 20×20?

12 Answer true or false: 'The number of squares on a chessboard is a square number.'

13 Work out

    a 4^3 **b** 3^3 **c** 8^3 **d** 9^3

14 Is 64 a square number or a cube number? Give clear reasons for your answer.

HWK 6M   **Main Book page 166**

1 What number when multiplied by itself gives

    a 81   **b** 144   **c** 225?

2 Find a pair of square numbers which give a total of:

    a 80   **b** 90   **c** 164   **d** 170

3 $2^3 = 2 \times 2 \times 2 = 8$, so 8 is a cube number. Which of these numbers are *not* cube numbers?

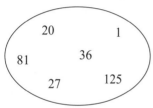

4 Find a pair of square numbers with a difference of:

    a 51   **b** 55   **c** 77   **d** 96

5 Use a calculator to find out which number, when multiplied by itself, gives a product of:

    a 2116   **b** 784   **c** 1024   **d** 6889

6 Vadim writes $(7 + 3)^2 = 7^2 + 3^2 = 49 + 9 = 58$. Is he correct? If not, explain why.

7 $13 \times 13 = 169$, so 169 is a square number. Find *four* square numbers which add together to make 169.

8 The square root of a number is the number which is multiplied by itself to give that number. The symbol for square root is $\sqrt{}$, so $\sqrt{9} = 3$ and $\sqrt{100} = 10$.
Work out

    a $\sqrt{81} - \sqrt{36}$ **b** $\sqrt{49} + \sqrt{1}$ **c** $\sqrt{(4^2 + \sqrt{81})}$

9 The difference between two cube numbers is 26. Write down the two cube numbers.

3.2 Further arithmetic

HWK 1M — **Main Book page 171**

1 Use any method to work out

a 46×37 b 69×69 c 425×28 d 372×43

2 Work out

a $14\overline{)742}$ b $27\overline{)702}$ c $44\overline{)1584}$

3 74 students each have to sit 13 exams. How many exams is this in total?

4 23 children each get 17 presents. How many presents is this altogether?

5 Find the missing number.

a $? \times 19 = 1026$ b $43 \times ? = 1204$

6 Which answer below is the odd one out?

A 32×12 B 18×22 C 16×24

7 A shop buys 29 skateboards for £1653. How much does each skateboard cost?

HWK 2M — **Main Book page 172**

Work out (there may be remainders)

1 $368 \div 17$ **2** $519 \div 24$ **3** 392×17

4 $637 \div 34$ **5** 186×48 **6** $473 \div 28$

7 Tins of baked beans are packed into boxes of 36. How many boxes are needed for 500 tins?

8 There are 217 people on a ship. The ship hits an iceberg and starts to sink. Each lifeboat can take 18 people. How many lifeboats are needed to get everyone safely off the ship?

9 Will makes models out of matches. A box of matches contains 42 matches. Will needs 3150 matches to make a castle. How many boxes of matches will he need to buy?

10 Lauren spends £66 on each day of her 14 day holiday. How much does she spend in total?

11 Jess has 414 plants. She wants to place them in 23 rows. How many plants could she place in each row?

12 Simon's heart beats 81 times each minute. How many times will his heart beat in a quarter of an hour?

13 If 4964 ÷ 68 = 73, write down the value of 73 × 68.

14 John sells 38 computer games at £46 each and 73 DVDs at £13 each. Marcia sells 56 DVDs at £12 each and 45 computer games at £45 each. Who takes most money? Show full working out.

HWK 3M ――――――――――――――――――――――――――――― **Main Book page 173**

1 Work out
   a 0.3 × 0.6   **b** 16.8 ÷ 6   **c** 0.8 × 0.07
   d 9 − 2.14   **e** 0.04²   **f** 39.69 ÷ 7

2 Six magazines cost £16.20. How much do eight magazines cost?

3 Work out the perimeter of the pentagon shown opposite.

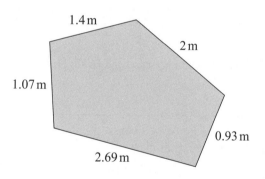

4 Jamie says that 20.8 × 3.1 is equal to 644.8. Aimeé says that 20 × 3 = 60 so Jamie has put the decimal point in the wrong place. *Explain* why you think Aimeé is likely to be correct.

5 Show that 0.7 × 0.3 = 12 − 11.79

6 Arrange the numbers in order of size, smallest first.
   a 0.89, 0.81, 0.093, 0.8, 0.72
   b 0.1, 0.32, 0.02, 0.23, 0.024
   c 5.27, 5.01, 5.1, 5.32, 5.12

7 Given that 42.75 ÷ 9 = 4.75, write down the values of:
   a 4.75 × 9   **b** 4.275 ÷ 9   **c** 47.5 × 9

3.3 Averages and range

HWK 1M ───────────────────────── **Main Book page 177**

For each list of numbers in questions **1** to **4**, find (a) the mean, (b) the median, (c) the mode and (d) the range.

1 3, 7, 9, 5, 3, 9, 9, 2, 7, 9, 3

2 120, 110, 108, 112, 120

3 15, 11, 13, 19, 13, 15, 11, 15

4 8, 5, 7, 3, 9, 1, 3, 4, 3, 7

5 The total weight of 7 children is 294 kg. Find the mean weight of the children.

6
4,	6,	6,	5,	7,	5,	4
6,	5,	8,	6,	4,	8,	5
4,	5,	7,	5,	6,	7,	4
7,	8,	5,	6,	5,	4,	7

The shoe sizes of a class of 28 pupils are shown in this box. Find the modal shoe size (the mode).

7 Kyle plays a computer game 9 times. His scores are shown below.

8290, 8200, 8247, 8315, 8956, 8721, 7460, 8194, 7278

Louise plays the computer game 7 times. Her scores are shown below.

9478, 8493, 7638, 8004, 8195, 7419, 9316

Which player has the greater median score and by how much?

HWK 1E ───────────────────────── **Main Book page 178**

1 The ages of some dogs in a kennel were 7, 3, 5, 3, 10, 2 and the ages of some cats were 5, 6, 9, 8.

    a Find the mean age for the dogs.

    b Find the mean age for the cats.

    c Find the mean age for all 10 animals.

2 'The modes for the numbers 3, 3, 3, 4, 4, 5, 5, 6, 6, 6, 7, 7, 7, 8 are 3, 6 and 7.'
Is this statement true or false?

3 Callum throws a dice eight times and his grandfather gives him a £1 coin if the mean score is equal to 3. The dice scores are shown below.

Does Callum win £1?

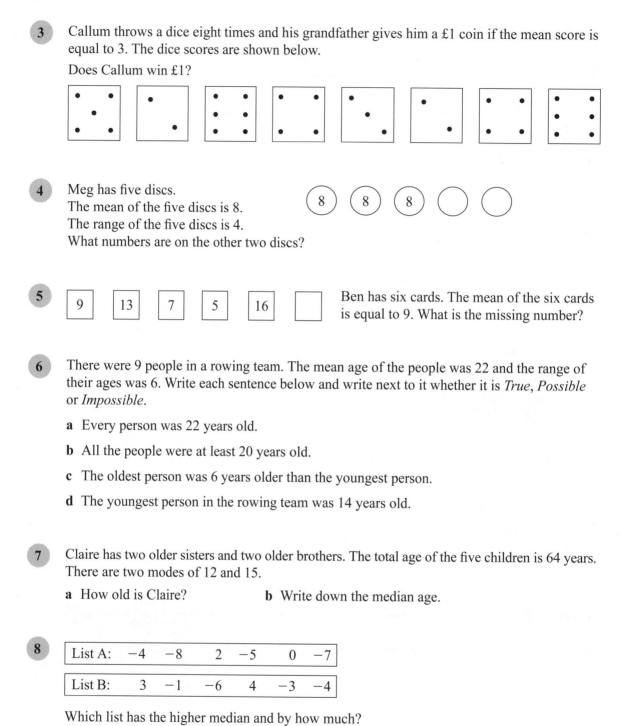

4 Meg has five discs.
The mean of the five discs is 8.
The range of the five discs is 4.
What numbers are on the other two discs?

5 | 9 | 13 | 7 | 5 | 16 | |

Ben has six cards. The mean of the six cards is equal to 9. What is the missing number?

6 There were 9 people in a rowing team. The mean age of the people was 22 and the range of their ages was 6. Write each sentence below and write next to it whether it is *True*, *Possible* or *Impossible*.

a Every person was 22 years old.

b All the people were at least 20 years old.

c The oldest person was 6 years older than the youngest person.

d The youngest person in the rowing team was 14 years old.

7 Claire has two older sisters and two older brothers. The total age of the five children is 64 years. There are two modes of 12 and 15.

a How old is Claire? **b** Write down the median age.

8

| List A: | −4 | −8 | 2 | −5 | 0 | −7 |

| List B: | 3 | −1 | −6 | 4 | −3 | −4 |

Which list has the higher median and by how much?

1 11 children in Year 7 and 11 children in Year 10 were asked how many pints of milk they drank in an 'average' week. The results are recorded below:

Year 7: 2 5 3 7 5 0 1 4 0 2 5

Year 10: 9 3 2 6 9 5 7 0 5 2 12

a Work out the median and range for Year 7.

b Work out the median and range for Year 10.

c Copy and complete the statement below:

'The median for Year 7 is (greater/smaller) than the median for Year 10 and the range for Year 7 is (greater/smaller) than the range for Year 10. This means the results for Year 7 are (more/less) spread out.'

2 The charts below show how many goals were scored in football matches one weekend in the Premiership and in the Championship.

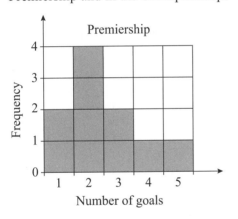

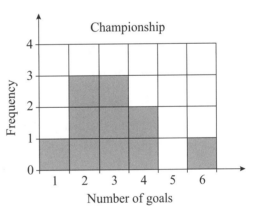

a Work out the mean and range for the Premiership.

b Work out the mean and range for the Championship.

c Write a sentence to compare the number of goals scored in the Premiership and in the Championship.

3 The times (in seconds) for two sprinters for their last six races are shown below.

| Kelly | 12.7 | 12.8 | 12.9 | 12.7 | 12.9 | 12.8 |
| Anna | 12.9 | 13.6 | 12.3 | 13.1 | 13.4 | 13.3 |

a The sprinter with the lowest mean time is to be chosen to run for their team. Who is chosen? Show all working out.

b Suggest a different way to choose the sprinter to run for their team.

74

3.4 Displaying and interpreting data

1 This graph shows the passengers on a bus.

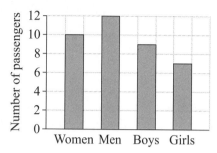

a How many women were on the bus?

b How many boys were on the bus?

c How many adults were on the bus?

d How many more women than girls were passengers?

e How many passengers were there altogether?

2 The members of a football club voted for the colour of their new kit. They chose from red, blue, gold and white. These are the results of the vote.

G B G R W G B R

R W R G G B R G

G R G B R W G R

B G W R G R B G

a Copy and complete the frequency table.

b Draw a bar chart to show the results.

Colour	Tally	Frequency
R	ЖЖ ЖЖ	10
B		
G		
W		

3 This bar chart shows the number of vowels in the first page of a book.

a Which was the most common vowel?

b Which was the least common vowel?

c How many As were there?

d How many Us were there?

e Which letter appeared half as often as E?

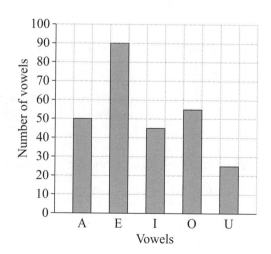

4 **a** Ask as many people as you can to tell you how many portions of fruit and vegetables they eat on an average day.

   b Use the results to make a frequency table.

   c Draw a bar chart to show the results.

   d What are the most portions eaten?

   e What are the least portions eaten?

   f Do you think these people eat enough fruit and vegetables? Explain why you think this.

HWK 2M ━━━━━━━━━━━━━━━━━━━━━━━━━━━━━ **Main Book page 188**

1 25 people are asked how many DVDs they have. The results are shown below.

15	21	41	43	38
8	23	34	47	16
22	38	43	20	6
33	21	19	8	23
34	12	43	16	37

Draw an ordered stem and leaf diagram.
Three entries are shown below.

Stem	Leaf
0	
1	5
2	1
3	
4	1

Remember the key, for example: | 1 | 2 means 12 |

2 The stem and leaf diagrams below show the weights of the players in two rugby teams.

Halford

Stem	Leaf
8	3 8 9
9	2 5 6 6 8
10	6 7 7
11	3 4 6
12	1

Key
9 | 5 means 95 kg

Malby

Stem	Leaf
8	0 2
9	4 8 9
10	6 7 7 7
11	2 5 5 8
12	4 9

Key
10 | 7 means 107 kg

   a Find the range and median weight of the rugby players for each team.

   b Write two sentences to compare the weights of the rugby players in each team. (One sentence should involve how spread out the weights are (range) and the second sentence should involve an average (median).)

3 **a** The numbers shown below give the ages of 30 people on a train between Birmingham and Derby. Draw an ordered stem and leaf diagram to show this data.

24	48	17	58	52	40	64	57	69	28
67	58	32	66	13	68	59	37	10	66
63	21	19	48	57	69	17	58	67	24

b What proportion (fraction) of the people were over 60 years old?

HWK 3M ── **Main Book page 191**

1 The frequency diagram opposite shows the heights of a group of children.

a How many children have a height between 150 and 155 cm?

b How many children are there altogether?

c How many children are less than 145 cm tall?

d What proportion (fraction) of the children are less than 140 cm tall?

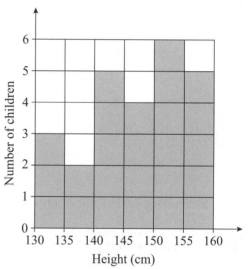

2 The ages of some people in a café are recorded as shown below.

38 12 63 18 42 87 56 55 72 8 19 26

82 59 13 73 23 68 31 17 44 12 95 48

a Put the ages into groups.

b Draw a frequency diagram.

c What fraction of the people are between 40 and 79 years old?

Age, A	Frequency
$0 \leqslant A < 20$	
$20 \leqslant A < 40$	
$40 \leqslant A < 60$	
$60 \leqslant A < 80$	
$80 \leqslant A < 100$	

3 The temperature in a centrally heated house is recorded every hour from 06:00 till 21:00. The results are shown below.

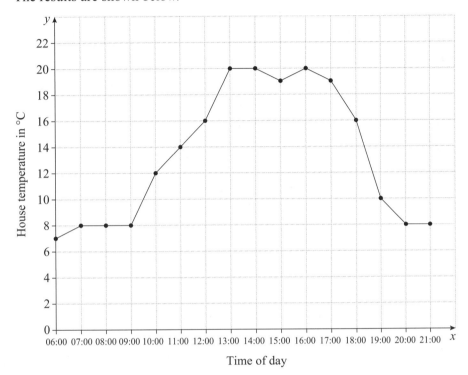

Time of day

a What was the temperature at 16:00?
b What was the temperature at 10:00?
c What was the temperature at 12:30?
d Write down the two times when the temperature was 16 °C.
e When do you think the central heating was switched on?
f Write down the two times when the temperature was 10 °C.
g When do you think the central heating was switched off?

HWK 4M ———————————————————————— **Main Book page 193**

1 56 people were asked what their favourite fruit was.
The results are shown by the pie chart.

a What fraction of the people preferred grapes?

b Copy and fill in this table.

Fruit	apples	oranges	grapes	strawberries
Number of people				

c If you were drawing the above pie chart, what angle would you use to draw the 'apples' sector?

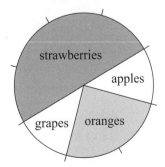

2 72 children were asked what their favourite colour was.
The results are shown by the pie chart.

a What fraction of the children chose blue?

b What fraction of the children chose yellow?

c How many children chose green?

d How many children chose yellow?

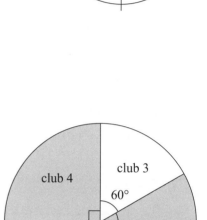

3 90 children were asked what their favourite sport is.

45 children chose football
15 children chose rugby
30 children chose hockey

Draw and label a pie chart to show these results.

4 A laundry firm washes towels for 4 leisure clubs.
The pie chart shows how 420 towels are
shared between the 4 leisure clubs.
Leisure club 3 needs 65 towels.
Will the laundry firm provide
leisure club 3 with enough towels?
Give clear reasons for your answer.

5 Some children were asked to state their favourite animal.
The results are shown by the pie charts below.

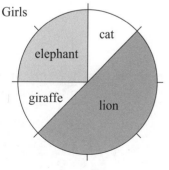

There were 80 girls.

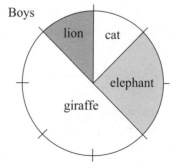

There were 64 boys.

Anna says 'The same number of boys and girls chose elephant'.
Harry says 'More girls than boys chose elephant'.

a Use both charts to explain whether Anna is correct.

b Use both charts to explain whether Harry is correct.

3 Some people were asked to name their favourite city in Europe. The results are shown by the pie charts below.

Men

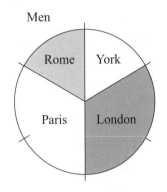

There were 180 men.

Women

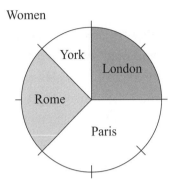

There were 120 women.

Marie says 'The same number of men and women prefer Rome'.

David says 'More women than men prefer Rome'.

a Use both charts to explain whether Marie or David is correct.

b Did more or less men than women prefer York? *Explain* your answer.

3.5 Probability 1

HWK 1M/2M ──────────────────────────→ **Main Book page 200**

1

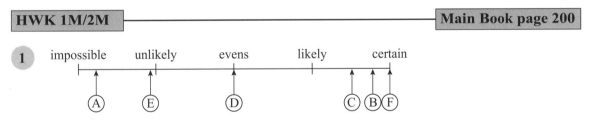

This is a probability scale. Some events are listed below. Write down which events are shown in the correct place on the probability scale above.

a You will get married next week.

b You will have a birthday in the next year.

c Your teacher will win the Lottery and retire to the Bahamas.

d When a coin is tossed it will show 'tails'.

e The sun will rise tomorrow.

f In the next TV series, Doctor Who will defeat the aliens and save the planet!

2 Draw this probability scale.

impossible   unlikely   evens   likely   certain

Draw an arrow to show the chance of the events below happening.

a A baby will be born somewhere in the world today.

b The next match a football team play will be a home game.

c Next time you roll a dice, you will get an even number.

d You will grow an extra leg tonight then win the 100 m race in the next Olympics.

e You will get at least one birthday card when you have your next birthday.

f You will see your headteacher before you get to school on your next school day.

3

impossible   unlikely   evens   likely   certain

0   0.1   0.2   0.3   0.4   0.5   0.6   0.7   0.8   0.9   1

Look at the events in questions **1** and **2** and for each one estimate the probability of it occurring using a probability from 0 to 1. (For example: question **2** **b** might be 'about 0.5')

4 Brianna and Rishi are playing darts. Brianna throws her first dart and hits the bullseye. Rishi says that this means he will hit the bullseye when he throws his first dart. Comment on what he has said.

5 Copy the probability scale in question **2**.

Think of four events and show where they would be on the probability scale. In your next lesson, ask another person if they agree with where you have placed your events on the scale.

HWK 3M ————————————————————————— **Main Book page 202**

1 Get a shoe.

2 Spin the shoe in the air and see if it lands 'the right way up', i.e. the heel on the bottom.

3 You must do this 50 times. Each time is called a 'trial' and you must record each time the shoe lands the 'right way up' (a 'success').

A tally chart like the one below may help.

Number of trials	Number of successes
ЖⅠ ⅠⅠⅠ	ⅠⅠⅠ

4 Use a calculator to work out the experimental probability that a shoe will land the 'right way up' when it is thrown in the air.

Reminder:

$$\text{experimental probability} = \frac{\text{number of successes}}{\text{total number of trials}}$$

'Experimental probability' is sometimes called the 'relative frequency'.

HWK 4M ──────────────────────────── **Main Book page 203**

1  Using this spinner, what is the probability of getting:

a the number 7   **b** the number 5

c an even number   **d** a multiple of 4

e a factor of 6?

2   Tania shuffles these cards then picks one out. What is the probability that she picks:

a the letter H

b the letter M

c a vowel?

3 8 football clubs are in the draw for the quarter-finals of the FA Cup.

Arsenal	Liverpool
Newcastle Utd	West Ham Utd
Everton	Chelsea
Manchester Utd	Manchester City

What is the probability that the first club to be chosen will be West Ham?

4 There are 10 beads in a bag.

I take out one bead. Work out the probability of taking out:

a   **b**   **c**

82

5 I roll an ordinary dice. Find the probability that it lands on:

a 4   **b** 2   **c** more than 3

6 There are 20 beads in a bag. 10 beads are blue, 3 beads are red, 2 beads are green and 5 beads are yellow.

I take out one bead. Find the probability of:

a taking out a red bead   **b** taking out a blue bead

c taking out a yellow bead   **d** taking out a green bead

e taking out a blue or red bead   **f** taking out a black bead.

7 Bag A contains 3 red beads and 3 yellow beads. Bag B contains 12 red beads and 4 yellow beads. Diya takes one bead from each bag. From which bag is she *more likely* to take a yellow bead? Give a reason for your answer.

8 There are 25 fish in a tank. 8 fish are gold. 12 fish are red.
The rest of the fish are yellow. I catch one fish. Find the probability of:

a catching a red fish

b catching a gold fish

c catching a yellow or red fish

d catching a gold, yellow or red fish.

9 Carson has a box of dark and milk chocolates. If he randomly takes one chocolate, the probability of it being a milk chocolate is $\frac{7}{10}$. Carson does, in fact, take one chocolate.

If he took another chocolate, explain why the probability of it being a milk chocolate would no longer be $\frac{7}{10}$.

UNIT 4

4.1 Percentages

HWK 1M — **Main Book page 222**

1 Copy and fill in the empty boxes.

a $48\% = \dfrac{\Box}{100} = \dfrac{\Box}{25}$

b $\dfrac{3}{20} = \dfrac{\Box}{100} = \Box\%$

c $0.37 = \dfrac{\Box}{100} = \Box\%$

d $0.4 = \dfrac{\Box}{10} = \dfrac{\Box}{100} = \Box\%$

e $\dfrac{4}{25} = \dfrac{\Box}{100} = 0.\Box\Box$

f $67\% = \dfrac{\Box}{100} = 0.\Box\Box$

2 Change these decimals into fractions. Cancel fractions down if you can.

a 0.6   b 0.24   c 0.59   d 0.35   e 0.64

3 Change these percentages into decimals.

a 49%   b 40%   c 8%   d 13%   e 85%

4 How much of this rectangle is shaded?   (45%)   or   (0.35)

5 Coleen sells 200 ice creams. 88 of the ice creams are chocolate.

a What fraction of the ice creams sold are chocolate?

b What percentage of the ice creams sold are *not* chocolate?

6 Which fractions are equivalent to the given decimal?

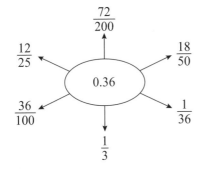

7   Ben says that 7% is 0.7 as a decimal. Explain clearly whether Ben is correct or not.

8   Which number is the larger? $\frac{2}{25}$ or   9%

9   Which number is the larger? $\frac{13}{20}$ or   0.64

10   Holly spends 0.3 of her money on a meal and $\frac{7}{25}$ of her money on books. What percentage of her money does she have left over?

11   There are five pairs of equivalent numbers below. Match each pair and write them down.

$\frac{4}{25}$ 95%   0.75   0.16   20%

$\frac{19}{20}$ 0.3 $\frac{1}{5}$ 30% $\frac{3}{4}$

12   Change the numbers below into percentages then write each list of numbers in order of size, smallest first.

a $\frac{3}{10}$, 0.4, $\frac{1}{4}$ **b** $\frac{2}{5}$, 38%, 0.39   **c**   0.7, $\frac{18}{25}$, 69%

HWK 2M   **Main Book page 224**

1   What percentage of this shape is shaded?

2   Draw your own shape and shade in exactly 70%.

3 What percentage of these shapes are stars?

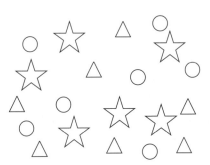

4 Terry has finished $\frac{2}{5}$ of his homework. What *percentage* of his homework does he still have to do?

5 Carol has washed $\frac{7}{20}$ of her car. What *percentage* of her car does she still have to wash?

6 Donna has used up $66\frac{2}{3}\%$ of her petrol. What *fraction* of her petrol does she have left?

7 Write down as a percentage how full each tube is.

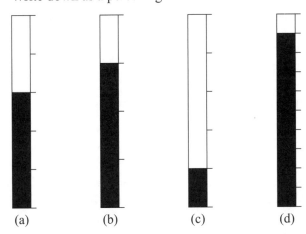

(a)   (b)   (c)   (d)

8 Holly owns 12 spanners. She uses 3 of these spanners when mending her bike. What percentage of the spanners did she use?

9 $\frac{3}{4}$ of the people on a bus are female. What percentage of the people are male?

10 The table below shows how many animals a farmer has.

Animal	cow	chicken	sheep	goat
Number	17	10	20	3

Work out the percentage difference in the number of sheep compared with the number of chickens.

86

1 Find the odd one out

a 30% of £80 **b** 75% of £32 **c** $33\frac{1}{3}$% of £45

2 Alan scores in 70% of the football matches that he plays in. One season Alan plays in 40 football matches. How many matches does he score in?

3 240 people are on a train. 40% of the people get off at Manchester and 15% get off at Birmingham. How many people are now on the train if nobody else gets on?

4 Jackie weighs 70 kg. She follows a diet and loses 5% of her weight. How much does she weigh now?

5 Nazim has a puppy which is 32 cm long. Over the next few weeks the puppy grows by 25%. How long is the puppy now?

6 Abbie has 600 building blocks. Her uncle gives her a set of building blocks at Christmas. This increases her number of blocks by 20%. How many building blocks does she have now?

7

Shirt £40 30% off   Shoes £60 40% off   Trousers £45 $33\frac{1}{3}$% off   Coat £80 55% off

Noel has £35 to spend in the sales. Which of the above items could he buy if he wanted to?

8 Josh earns £300 each week and is given a pay increase of 15%. Diane earns £340 each week and is given a pay increase of 5%. Who earns the most money now and by how much?

9 Norman is trying to sell his car for £8000 but nobody will buy it. He reduces the price by 15% and Alice buys the car from him. How much does Alice pay for the car?

10 A sofa costs £1420 plus 20% VAT (Value Added Tax). What is the total price of the sofa?

11 Make up your own question which uses the numbers £80, 20% and the word 'decreases'.

Use a calculator when needed.

1 **a** Find 1% of £3200 **b** Find 7% of £3200

2 Work out

 a 9% of £5300 **b** 24% of £470 **c** 42% of £650

3 12% of £49 is smaller than 14% of £47 .

What is the difference between them? (i.e. subtract the answers)

4 Mrs Williams has a fortune of £2 348 800. She gives 37% of her fortune to a charity. How much money does she have left?

5 **a** Increase £6800 by 6%. **b** Decrease £560 by 8%.
 c Reduce £730 by 14%. **d** Increase £310 by 43%.

6 Jackie has a piece of wood 120 cm long. She cuts off 16% of the wood. How long is the piece of wood now?

7 Hal has £230 to spend on holiday. If he spends 84% of his money, how much does he have left?

8

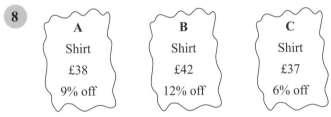

A	B	C
Shirt	Shirt	Shirt
£38	£42	£37
9% off	12% off	6% off

 a Which shirt is the cheapest to buy?
 b Which shirt is the most expensive to buy?
 c What is the difference between the cheapest and the most expensive price?

9 Helen is 1.5 m tall. How tall is she if she grows another 6%?

10 Ollie buys a 330 ml can of cola and drinks 72% of the cola. Brooke then takes the can and drinks 70% of the remaining cola. How many millilitres of cola are now left in the can?

4.2 Proportion and ratio

HWK 1M ———————————————————— **Main Book page 232**

1 A 160 g sausage roll contains 40 g of meat. What proportion of the sausage roll is meat?

2 There are 50 children in a playground. 29 children are girls. What proportion of the children are boys?

88

3 What proportion of this rectangle is shaded?

4 What proportion of these faces seem to be happy?

5 £40 can be exchanged for 65 euros. How many euros can be exchanged for £160?

6 If £1 is worth 1.88 dollars, how many dollars will you get for £1000?

7 The pie chart shows the favourite hot drink for the teachers in a school.

   a What proportion prefer tea?

   b What proportion prefer coffee?

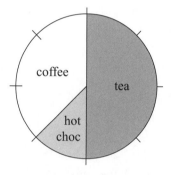

8 A painter uses 108 pots of paint to finish painting 24 houses. How many pots of paint will he use to finish painting 72 houses?

9 12 dogs eat 22 tins of dog food in 6 days. How many tins of dog food would 6 dogs eat in 12 days?

10 A baker has 420 g of plain flour. A recipe for 6 cakes requires 140 g of plain flour. How many cakes can the chef make?

HWK 2M ——————————————————— **Main Book page 233**

1 Find the cost of 8 plates if 2 plates cost £12.

2 Four lemons cost 92p. How much will 7 lemons cost?

3 Six footballs cost £48. How much will 5 footballs cost?

4   Find the cost of 9 pens if 5 pens cost £6.50.

5   If 8 computers cost £3600, how much will 10 computers cost?

6   Five digital radios cost £235. How much will 3 digital radios cost?

7   The total cost of 9 exercise books is £4.68. What is the total cost of 8 exercise books?

8   A car travels 200 km in 120 minutes. How long will it take to travel 50 km?

9   Which box of granola opposite
is the better value?
Explain your answer fully.

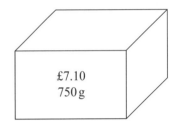

10   In a supermarket you can buy 4 toilet rolls for £1.68 or 6 toilet rolls for £2.58. Which is the cheaper price per toilet roll?

11   In a fruit and veg shop you can buy 5 onions for 85p or 8 onions for £1.12. Which is the best deal per onion?

12

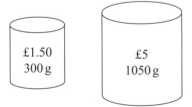

Which tin of fruit is the better value?
Explain your answer fully.

HWK 3M   **Main Book page 235**

1   There are 19 adults on a bus. 13 are women and 6 are men. Write down the ratio of women to men.

2   There are 43 animals in a field. 26 are sheep and the rest are cows. Write down the ratio of sheep to cows.

3      Write down the ratio of black circles to white circles.

4  Write down the ratio of black circles to white circles.

5 Copy this diagram. Colour it in so that the ratio of black squares to white squares is 3 : 1.

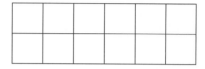

6 Write these ratios in simplified form.

   a 2 : 16   **b** 8 : 24   **c** 20 : 15   **d** 42 : 28   **e** 12 : 24 : 30

7 There are 28 children in a class. $\frac{4}{7}$ of the children are boys. Write down the girl to boy ratio.

8 Is the ratio 18 : 6 *equivalent* to 3 : 1?

9 The ratio of footballs to tennis balls in a PE store is 3 : 10. What fraction of the balls are tennis balls?

10 Complete the empty boxes to make the ratios *equivalent* to each other.

   a 25 : 15 = 5 : ☐   **b** 14 : 21 = ☐ : 3   **c** 40 : 5 = ☐ : 1

   d 70 : 90 = 7 : ☐   **e** 24 : 16 = ☐ : 2   **f** 27 : 36 = 3 : ☐

11 Consider the numbers from 1 to 20. Write down the ratio of how many prime numbers there are to how many non-prime numbers there are.

HWK 4M ———————————————————————————— **Main Book page 236**

1 Share £60 in the ratio   **a** 2 : 1   **b** 7 : 3   **c** 2 : 3

2 Share £48 in the ratio   **a** 1 : 3   **b** 5 : 3   **c** 1 : 5

3 Sid and Aisha share 24 chocolates in the ratio 1 : 2. How many chocolates does each person get?

4 Mrs Dennis gives her two children £135 in the ratio 7 : 2. How much money is each share?

5 The ratio of black sheep to white sheep in a field is 4 : 7. If the total number of sheep is 55, how many white sheep are there?

6 The tables below show how two sums of money were split.

£350
Alan : Max
5 : 2

£520
Donna : Hilary
1 : 3

How much more money does Donna get than Max?

7 Jane does a survey and finds that the ratio of blue cars to red cars to yellow cars is 6 : 1 : 5. If there are 36 cars, how many cars of each colour are there?

8 Dan, Josh and Elaine have 775 little toy soldiers between them in the ratio 7 : 9 : 15. How many soldiers does each child have?

9 The ratio of men to women in a theatre is 5 : 1. What proportion of the people are women?

10 Bailey and Connor are given some money in the ratio 2 : 7. If Connor receives £84, how much does Bailey get?

4.3 Constructing triangles

HWK 1M — — — — — — — — — — — — — — — **Main Book page 244**

You must use a protractor and ruler to construct each diagram below.

1 **a** Draw PQ = 8 cm and
P$\hat{Q}$R = 55° as shown below.

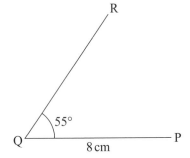

b Put the centre of the protractor on P and
measure an angle of 60° as shown below.

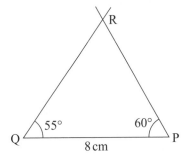

c Measure Q$\hat{R}$P. It should be 65°.

2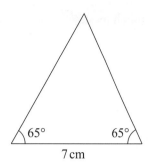

3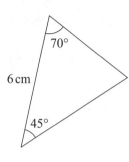

4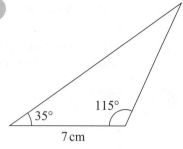

5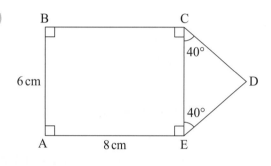

Measure the length AD.

6 Kaitlyn and Jason both cycle to school. They cycle at the same steady speed. Construct the diagram opposite using a scale of 1 cm to 1 km.

If they both leave their home at the same time, who will get to school first?

Explain your answer fully.

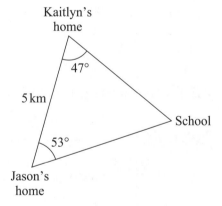

7 Construct the rhombus shown below.

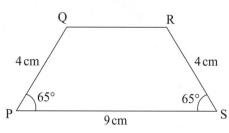

Measure PQ̂R.

1 Use a ruler and a pair of compasses to construct the triangles below. For each triangle, measure the angle x.

a
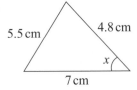

b
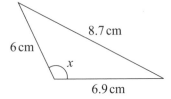

c
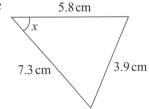

2 Construct triangle PQR where PQ = 4.9 cm, QR = 6.6 cm and PR = 7.2 cm. Measure QP̂R.

3 Construct the shapes below. For each shape, measure the angle x.

a
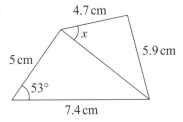

b
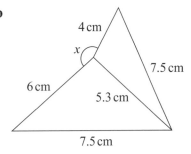

4.4 Two-dimensional shapes

1
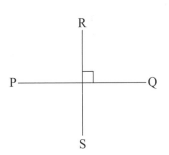

Answer true or false.

'PQ is perpendicular to RS'

94

2

C

E

B

Answer true or false.

'CD is perpendicular to EF'

A

D

F

3 **a** Write down the names of all the sides which are parallel to AB.

b Write down the names of all the sides which are parallel to AF.

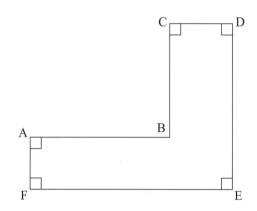

4 **a** How many parallel lines does this letter have?

b How many perpendicular lines does this letter have?

5 Copy this diagram.

a Draw a line through B which is perpendicular to AD.

b Draw a line through C which is parallel to the line you have just drawn.

c Is your last line parallel or perpendicular to AD?

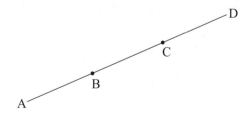

6 Draw a quadrilateral which has two parallel sides only.

7 Draw a five-sided shape which has two pairs of perpendicular sides but no parallel sides.

8 Name an object in this room which has at least two parallel sides.

9 Draw any design of your own which has at least two parallel lines and two perpendicular lines. If possible, show the parallel lines in one colour and the perpendicular lines in a different colour.

| **HWK 3M** | **Main Book page 252** |

1 Which triangle below is equilateral?

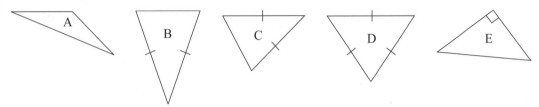

2 What is the name of a triangle with three different sides and three different angles?

3 Which quadrilateral below is a trapezium?

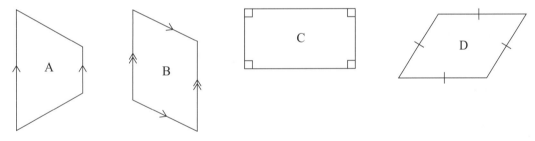

4 Draw a parallelogram (use a ruler!)

5 Name the shapes opposite which are hexagons.

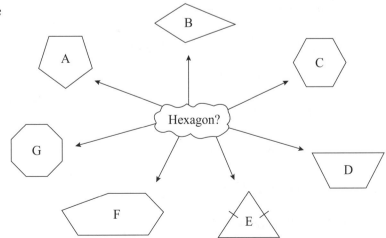

96

6 Draw any quadrilateral which has no parallel sides.

7 Write down the names of any quadrilaterals which have right angles inside them.

8 Draw a regular pentagon.

9 How many trapeziums can you see in this diagram?

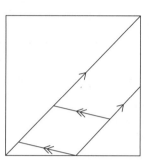

10 The broken lines opposite show the two *diagonals* of a quadrilateral. A *diagonal* joins opposite vertices (corners of a quadrilateral).

In which of the quadrilaterals listed below are the diagonals perpendicular to each other?

(square)   (kite)   (rectangle)   (rhombus)

Use diagrams to show the reasons for your answers.

4.5 Translation

HWK 1M ——————————————— **Main Book page 257**

1 What shape do you move to when you

a translate shape Q by $\begin{pmatrix} 2 \\ -2 \end{pmatrix}$

b translate shape S by $\begin{pmatrix} -2 \\ -3 \end{pmatrix}$

c translate shape R by $\begin{pmatrix} -6 \\ -3 \end{pmatrix}$

d translate shape Q by $\begin{pmatrix} 8 \\ -2 \end{pmatrix}$

e translate shape T by $\begin{pmatrix} -2 \\ 5 \end{pmatrix}$

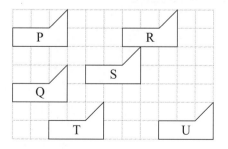

2

Use translation vectors to describe the following translations.

a A → C   **b** A → B

c D → A   **d** D → E

e B → D   **f** E → B

3 Shape A is translated to shape B by the vector $\begin{pmatrix} -1 \\ 4 \end{pmatrix}$. Write down the translation vector which translates shape B to shape A.

4

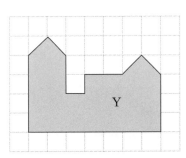

Use translation vectors to describe the following translations.

a A_1 to A_2 **b** R_1 to R_2

c T_1 to T_2 **d** P_2 to P_1

e A_2 to R_1 **f** T_2 to R_1

g T_2 to A_1 **h** A_1 to P_2

5

Draw shape Y.

Draw the image of Y after a translation by $\begin{pmatrix} 1 \\ 1 \end{pmatrix}$.

98

4.6 Reflection

HWK 1M/1E — Main Book page 260

Copy each diagram and shade in as many squares as necessary so that the final pattern has mirror lines shown by the broken lines. For each question, write down how many new squares were shaded in.

1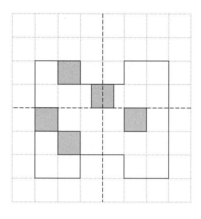

2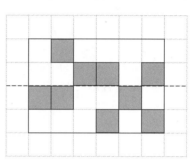

3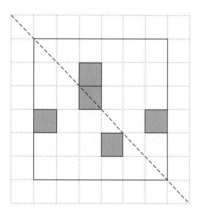

4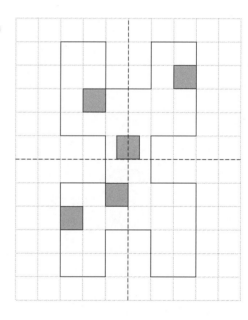

5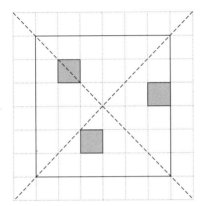

6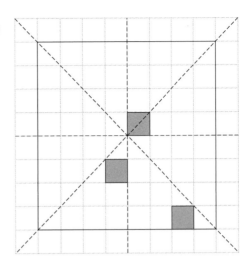

| HWK 2M | Main Book page 262 |

1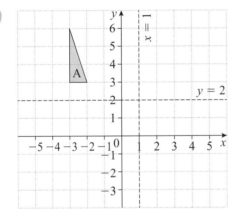

Copy the diagram.

a Reflect triangle A in the line $y = 2$.

b Reflect triangle A in the line $x = 1$.

2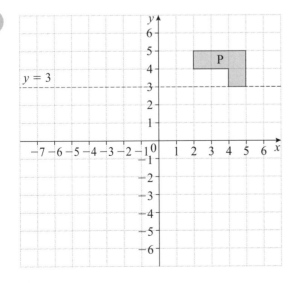

Copy the diagram.

a Reflect shape P in the line $y = 3$.

b Reflect shape P in the x-axis.

c Draw the vertical line $x = -1$.

d Reflect shape P in the line $x = -1$.

3 **a** Draw an *x*-axis from -2 to 5 and a *y*-axis from -6 to 6.

b Draw a rectangle with vertices at $(1, -4)$, $(4, -4)$, $(4, -5)$ and $(1, -5)$. Label this rectangle A.

c Reflect rectangle A in the line $y = -3$. Label the image B.

d Reflect rectangle B in the line $y = 1$. Label the image C.

4 Write down the equation of the mirror line for the following reflections.

a P to Q

b P to R

c R to S

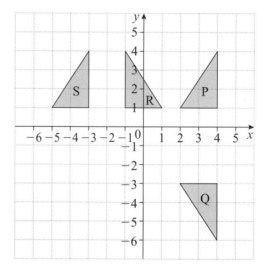

4.7 Rotation

HWK 1M ──────────────────────────────── **Main Book page 264**

Copy each diagram below and then draw its new position after it has been turned (you may use tracing paper).

1

A quarter turn
  clockwise

2

A half turn

3

A turn through
2 right angles

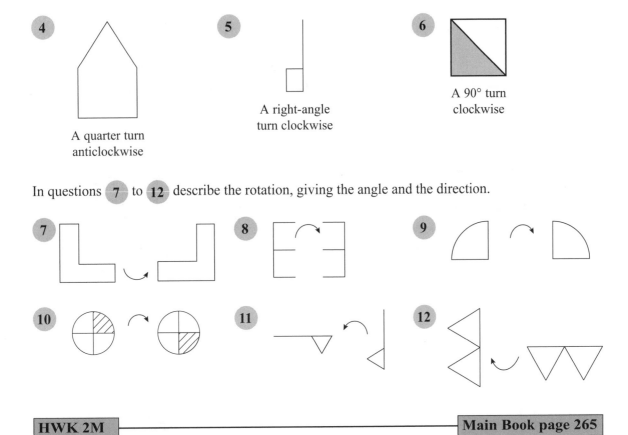

4 A quarter turn anticlockwise

5 A right-angle turn clockwise

6 A 90° turn clockwise

In questions **7** to **12** describe the rotation, giving the angle and the direction.

7

8

9

10

11

12

| HWK 2M | Main Book page 265 |

1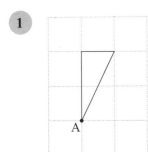

  a Copy this triangle on squared paper.

  b Draw the triangle after a quarter turn anticlockwise around the point A.

2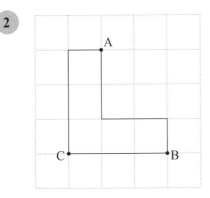

  a Copy this shape on squared paper.

  Draw the image of the shape:

  b after a 90° rotation anticlockwise about A

  c after a half turn about B

  d after a 90° rotation anticlockwise about C.

3

a Copy this shape on squared paper.
Draw the image of the shape:

b after a 90° rotation clockwise about P

c after a 180° rotation about Q.

4 The diagram shows some shapes which have
been rotated. Which shape do you get when you:

a rotate shape M 90° clockwise about A

b rotate shape R 90° clockwise about B

c rotate shape N 90° anticlockwise about C

d rotate shape R 180° about D?

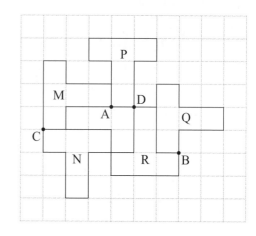

| **HWK 3M** | **Main Book page 266** |

Use tracing paper for the questions in this exercise.

1

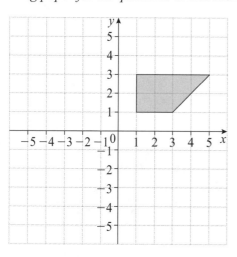

Copy the diagram opposite then rotate the
shape 180° about (0, 0).

2

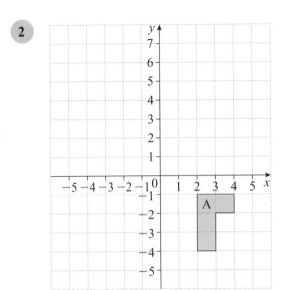

a Copy the diagram opposite.

b Rotate shape A 180° about (3, 1).
Label the image B.

c Rotate shape A 180° about (0, 0).
Label the image C.

3
a Draw *x* and *y* axes from −4 to 4.

b Draw a triangle with vertices at (−1, −2), (−4, −2) and (−1, −3). Label this triangle A.

c Rotate triangle A 90° clockwise about (0, 0). Label the image B.

d Rotate triangle B 180° about (0, 0). Label the image C.

e Triangle C can be rotated back to triangle A.
Write down the direction, angle of rotation and the coordinates of the centre of rotation.

4 A shape is rotated 60° anticlockwise about (1, 2). Write down in detail the rotation which will send the new shape back to its starting position. You must give the direction, angle of rotation and the coordinates of the centre of rotation.

HWK 4M/4E ──────────────────────────────── **Main Book page 268**

This shape fits onto itself four times when rotated through a complete turn.
It has *rotational symmetry* of *order* four.

1 For each diagram, decide whether or not the shape has *rotational symmetry*.
If yes, write down the *order*.

a   **b**   **c**   **d**

e   **f**   **g**   **h**

2

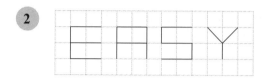

  a Which of these letters has no line of symmetry?

  b Which of these letters has rotational symmetry of order 2?

3 Draw a shape with line symmetry but no rotational symmetry.

4

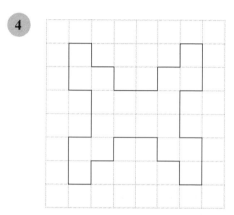

  a Does this shape have line symmetry? If so, how many lines?

  b Does this shape have rotational symmetry? If so, what is the order?

5 Copy each diagram and shade more squares so that the final design has rotational symmetry of the order stated.

a

order 4

b

order 2

c

order 4

UNIT 5

5.1 More algebra

Find the value of each expression below if $a = 4$ $b = 3$ $c = 8$

1 $4b$

2 $3a + 4b$

3 bc

4 $3b - a$

5 $9a + 2b + 4c$

6 $\dfrac{c}{a}$

7 $5(c - b)$

8 c^2

9 $b(a + c)$

10 $\dfrac{4b + 5a}{c}$

Simplify the expressions in questions **11** to **16** by collecting terms.

11 $6m + 4n + 3n - 3m$

12 $4y + 2w + y$

13 $3f + 2g - 2f + 2g$

14 $7a + 3 + 5a$

15 $9x + 2x + 3y - 6x$

16 $2p + 3q + 4 - 2q$

17 There are 36 people on a bus. At the cinema x people get off the bus and y people get on. Write down an expression for the number of people on the bus now.

18 What belongs in the empty box? $3a + a + 4b + \boxed{} = 4a + 5b$

19 $n \times n = 2n$ True or false?

20 Which expressions below are equal to $3y$?

$\boxed{y \times 3}$ $\boxed{y + 2y}$ $\boxed{y \times y \times y}$ $\boxed{4y - y}$ $\boxed{2y + 1}$

21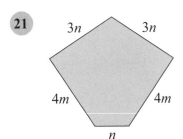

Write down an expression for the perimeter of this pentagon.

22 Simplify

a $5 \times p \times q$

b $9 \times m \times 4 \times n$

c $6 \times n \times 2 \times n$

23 Eli says that the expression $ab + c$ gives the same answer as $c + ba$. Is he correct? Give reasons for your answer.

24 Which expressions below are equal to $5a + 2b$?

| $3a + 2b + 2$ | $b + 5a + b$ | $4a + 3b + a - b$ | $6a + 2b - 1$ | $b + 5a + 2b$ |

HWK 2E   **Main Book page 290**

Find the value of each expression below if $m = 2$ $n = -3$ $p = 0$

1 mn **2** mp **3** $5n$ **4** $2m + 5n$ **5** $4n + p$

6 n^2 **7** $n + np$ **8** $6(m - n)$ **9** $n(3m - p)$ **10** mnp

11 $h = 2n + 7$
Find h when $n = 9$

12 $a = 6b - 8$
Find a when $b = 4$

13 $m = pq$
Find m when $p = 4$ and $q = -8$

14 $w = 7(c + 3d)$
Find w when $c = 9$ and $d = -1$

15 $y = x(x - 6)$
Find y when $x = 9$

16 $b = cp$
Find b when $c = 8$ and $p = -7$

17 $a = b(c - b)$
Find a when $b = -4$ and $c = 2$

18 $m = n^2 + 9$
Find m when $n = -4$

19 $q = 3w + 2y$
Find q when $w = -5$ and $y = 3$

20 $y = \dfrac{x^2}{m}$
Find y when $x = -6$ and $m = -9$

HWK 3M   **Main Book page 292**

Find the weight x by removing weights from both pans. Weights are in kg.

1 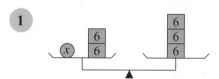   **2**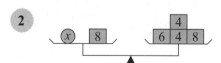

3 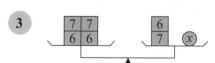   **4**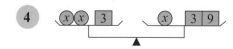

5 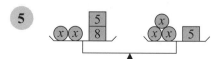   **6**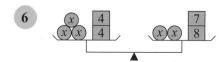

7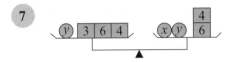

8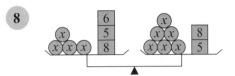

9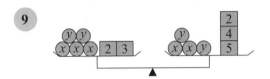

10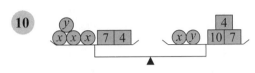

11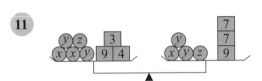

12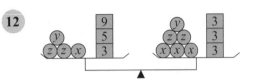

| HWK 4M/5M | Main Book page 293 |

Solve the equations below.

1 $n + 3 = 7$

2 $n - 5 = 6$

3 $n - 14 = 8$

4 $10 = n + 6$

5 $9 = n - 6$

6 $n - 10 = 12$

Questions **7** to **15** involve multiplication and division.

7 $3n = 18$

8 $7n = 35$

9 $24 = 3n$

10 $4n = 0$

11 $\dfrac{n}{4} = 9$

12 $\dfrac{n}{7} = 6$

13 $5n = 200$

14 $\dfrac{n}{8} = 6$

15 $12 = \dfrac{n}{3}$

In questions **16** to **30** find x.

16 $7x = 49$

17 $x - 6 = 4$

18 $19 = x + 7$

19 $\dfrac{x}{6} = 8$

20 $x + 34 = 60$

21 $9x = 108$

22 $32 = x - 17$

23 $18 = x + 18$

24 $15 = \dfrac{x}{3}$

25 $2x = 1$

26 $19x = 57$

27 $173 = x - 258$

28 $\dfrac{x}{8} = 10$

29 $450 = 3x$

30 $5 = 10x$

108

Solve the equations below to find x.

1 $4x + 1 = 13$ **2** $5x - 4 = 31$ **3** $4x - 6 = 26$

4 $4x - 7 = 33$ **5** $6x + 9 = 39$ **6** $8x - 7 = 1$

7 $7x + 8 = 71$ **8** $9x - 14 = 22$ **9** $10x - 70 = 130$

10 $8x - 11 = 5$ **11** $4x + 17 = 77$ **12** $3x - 39 = 36$

In questions **13** to **24** solve the equations to find n.

13 $3n - 13 = 5$ **14** $9n + 13 = 85$ **15** $25 + 5n = 275$

16 $16 + 4n = 32$ **17** $6n + 9 = 9$ **18** $8n - 20 = 36$

19 $4n - 25 = 15$ **20** $8n + 18 = 42$ **21** $12 + 5n = 512$

22 $20n - 7 = 33$ **23** $77 = 2n + 17$ **24** $23 = 5n - 22$

1   I think of a number n. I multiply the number by 6 and then add 5. The answer is 41. Write down an equation then find the value of n.

2   I think of a number n. I multiply the number by 7 and then subtract 13. The answer is 43. Write down an equation then find the value of n.

3   I think of a number n. I treble the number and then subtract 38. The answer is 37. Write down an equation then find the value of n.

4   I think of a number n. I multiply the number by 8 and then subtract 4. The answer is 52. Write down an equation and then find the value of n.

5 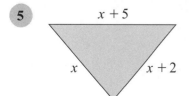

An expression for the perimeter of this triangle is

$$x + x + 5 + x + 2$$

The actual value of the perimeter is 34 cm
so $x + x + 5 + x + 2 = 34$
so $3x + 7 = 34$
Solve this equation to find the value of x.

6 The perimeter of this rectangle is 36 cm.
Write down an equation then find the value of *x*.

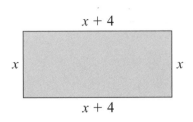

7 The perimeter of this rectangle is 48 cm.
Write down an equation then find the value of *x*.

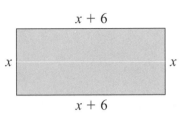

8 The length of a rectangle is 9 cm more than its width. If its perimeter is 42 cm, what is its width?

9 Write down an equation for the angles in this triangle then find the value of *x*.

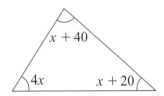

10 Lesley has four times as many marbles as Mark but then Lesley loses 3 of her marbles. If Lesley now has 17 marbles, how many marbles does Mark have?

HWK 7M	**Main Book page 296**

Solve the equations below.

1 $29 = 4x + 1$ **2** $41 = 6x - 7$ **3** $15 = 8x - 9$

4 $62 = 7x - 8$ **5** $107 = 6x + 17$ **6** $41 = 30x - 19$

7 $64 = 3x + 13$ **8** $45 = 24 + 3x$ **9** $5x + 17 = 17$

10 $120 = 4x - 8$ **11** $5x - 16 = 74$ **12** $91 = 19 + 6x$

In questions **13** to **21** find the value of the letter.

13 $8m + 5 = 53$ **14** $323 = 3w - 37$ **15** $29 + 5y = 94$

16 $4a - 270 = 730$ **17** $152 = 6p - 58$ **18** $79 = 47 + 4n$

19 $7b + 90 = 1000$ **20** $159 = 24 + 3x$ **21** $2q - 93 = 297$

110

Multiply out

1 $5(x + 4)$ **2** $3(a + 9)$ **3** $2(b - 7)$

4 $6(m - 3)$ **5** $8(y + 4)$ **6** $4(6 + n)$

7 $6(m + n)$ **8** $3(2x - 4)$ **9** $5(3p + 5)$

10 $8(4y - 5)$ **11** $6(2a + 3)$ **12** $2(x - y)$

13 $9(4 - q)$ **14** $3(2a + 5b)$ **15** $6(3m + 1)$

16 $7(3c + 2d)$ **17** $5(8w - 7)$ **18** $4(2a + b + 5)$

19 $9(2m - 9n)$ **20** $4(7p + 8q)$ **21** $3(8 + 3y - 7x)$

22

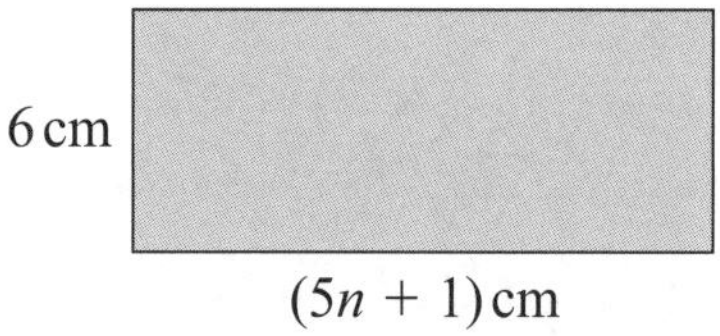

6 cm

(5n + 1) cm

The area of this rectangle
is $(30n + 1)\,\text{cm}^2$.
True or false?
Give a reason for your answer.

Expand

1 $a(b + d)$ **2** $m(y - w)$ **3** $n(p + 4)$

4 $p(q - 5)$ **5** $c(d - 8)$ **6** $x(y + 3)$

7 $b(5 + c)$ **8** $n(n + 7)$ **9** $a(a - 6)$

10 $p(3 + w)$ **11** $x(9 - x)$ **12** $4(3n + 2)$

13 $7(8a - 4)$ **14** $m(m - 2)$ **15** $5(3q - 9)$

16 $y(9 + y)$ **17** $b(4 - c)$ **18** $3(8w + 7)$

19 $4(3 + 6m)$ **20** $x(x - 4)$ **21** $a(7 - a)$

22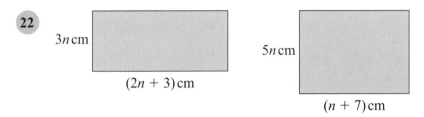

3*n* cm

(2*n* + 3) cm

5*n* cm

(*n* + 7) cm

  a Write down an expression for the total area of the two rectangles.
Multiply out any brackets.

  b Find the actual total area if *n* = 8.

23 A book costs £(4*n* − 3). Write down an expression for the total cost of *m* books.

5.2 Interpreting graphs

HWK 1M   **Main Book page 301**

1 This graph shows the number of people in a supermarket one day.

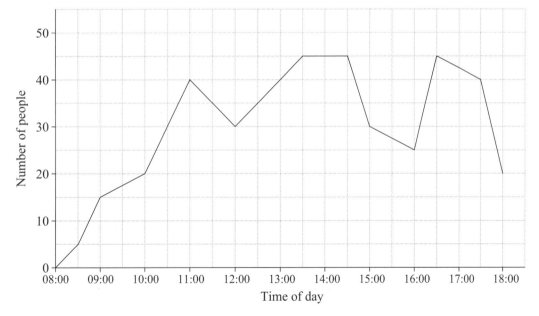

  a How many people were in the supermarket at
(i) 12:00   (ii) 10:30   (iii) 08:30?

  b At what time were 15 people in the supermarket?

  c At what two times were there 20 people in the supermarket?

  d How long did it take in the afternoon for the number of people to increase from 25 to 45?

2

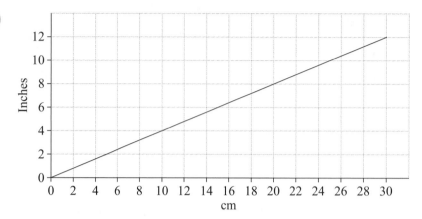

The graph above converts cm into inches.

a Convert into inches
   (i) 10 cm   (ii) 20 cm   (iii) 5 cm

b Which is longer: 15 cm or 7 inches?

3

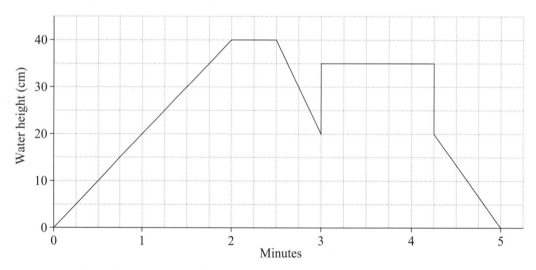

Meg runs a bath then gives her baby a quick bath. The graph above shows the water height during 5 minutes.

a What was the water height after 30 seconds?

b What was the water height after 1 minute 45 seconds?

c When did the baby go into the bath?

d How long was the baby in the bath for?

e What probably happened after $2\frac{1}{2}$ minutes?

f How long did the bath take to empty once the baby had been taken out of the bath?

1

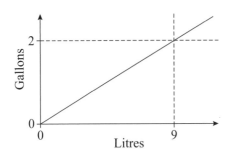

Draw a graph to convert litres into gallons. Draw a line through the point where 9 litres is equivalent to 2 gallons.

Use a scale of 1 cm to 1 litre across the page and 2 cm to 1 gallon up the page.

Use your graph to convert

a 0.6 gallons into litres

b 6.3 litres into gallons

2 Rob burns off 9 Kcal for every one minute on an exercise bike.

a Draw a graph to show what Rob burns off during 10 minutes on the exercise bike.

b Use your graph to find out how long it takes Rob to burn off 31.5 Kcal.

c Use your graph to find out how many Kcal Rob has used after 7 minutes 30 seconds.

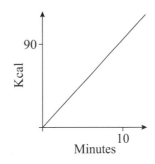

3 A city taxi firm charges £2 for each call-out. The total cost then depends on the journey time, as shown in the table below.

Journey time (minutes)	0	2	4	6	8	10
Cost (£)	2	3	4	5	6	7

a Draw a graph to show this information.

b Use your graph to find the total cost of making a 7-minute journey.

c Estimate the total cost of a 14-minute journey.

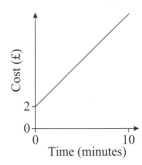

1 The graph shows a car journey from Manchester.

a How far is it from Leeds to Sheffield?

b For how long does the car stop in Leeds?

c How much further is it to Leeds at 09:30?

d What is the speed of the car from Manchester to Leeds?

e How long does the car take to get from Leeds to Sheffield?

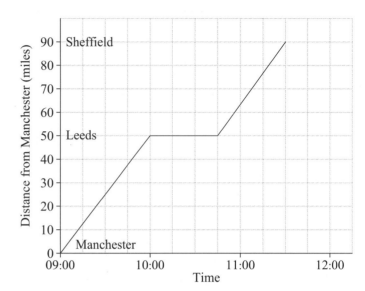

2 The graph shows a car journey from Taunton.

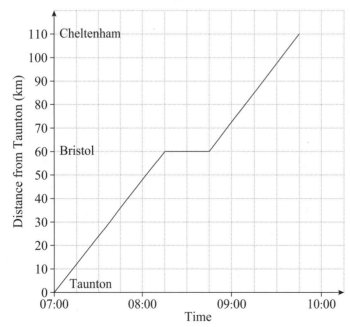

a When did the car leave Bristol?

b How far is it from Bristol to Cheltenham?

c How far from Taunton was the car after 2 hours 15 minutes?

d Find the speed of the car from Bristol to Cheltenham.

3

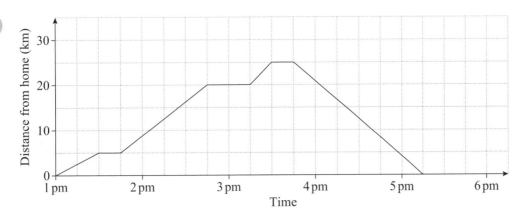

Callum goes for a bike ride. The graph shows how far he was from his home.

a How long did he stop for at 2.45 pm?

b At what time did he set off for home?

c How many times did he stop on his journey?

d What was his speed on his journey between his first stop and his second stop?

5.3 Number review

HWK 1M   Main Book page 310

1   Answer true or false.

   a 5 is a factor of 10   **b** 4 is a factor of 18

   c 6 is a prime number   **d** 30 is a multiple of 6

2   Copy and complete:

   a All the factors of 8 are 1, 2, ☐ and 8

   b All the factors of 20 are 1, 2, 4, 5, ☐ and ☐

   c All the factors of 30 are 1, 2, ☐, 5, ☐, ☐, ☐ and 30

3   Write down the first six multiples of 5.

4   Write down all the prime numbers between 10 and 20.

5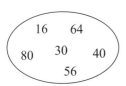
   16   64
   80   30   40
      56

   a Which number is not a multiple of 8?

   b Which number is a factor of 32?

6 Is 39 a prime number? Give a reason for your answer.

7 Write down all the factors of 48.

8 *Explain* whether an even number can be a prime number.

HWK 2M ———————————————————————— **Main Book page 312**

1 **a** Write down the first five multiples of 4.
  b Write down the first five multiples of 6.
  c Write down the Lowest Common Multiple (L.C.M.) of 4 and 6.

2 Find the L.C.M. of
  a 5 and 8 **b** 7 and 4 **c** 8 and 6

3 Write down the smallest prime number which is larger than 50.

4 **a** Write down all the factors of 40.
  b Write down all the factors of 50.
  c Write down the Highest Common Factor (H.C.F.) of 40 and 50.

5 Find the H.C.F. of
  a 15 and 35 **b** 12 and 20 **c** 25 and 40

6 Continue this factor tree then write 140
as a product of its prime factors.

7 Write the following numbers as products of their prime factors by drawing factor trees first.
  a 120 **b** 210 **c** 546

8 A number is written as the product of its prime factors: $3 \times 3 \times 7 \times 13$.
Write down the number.

9 The factor trees for 130
and 273 are shown opposite.
Write down the H.C.F. of
130 and 273.

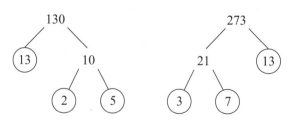

10 By finding all the factors, explain why 4 is different from 2, 3 and 5.

1 Which fraction is not equivalent to the other three fractions? $\left(\frac{8}{12}\right)$ $\left(\frac{4}{6}\right)$ $\left(\frac{10}{16}\right)$ $\left(\frac{20}{30}\right)$

2 Cancel down each fraction to its lowest terms.

a $\frac{10}{25}$ **b** $\frac{14}{20}$ **c** $\frac{4}{16}$ **d** $\frac{15}{18}$ **e** $\frac{9}{24}$ **f** $\frac{12}{30}$

3 Answer true or false.

a $\frac{4}{5} = 0.8$ **b** $\frac{7}{100} = 0.7$ **c** $\frac{5}{20} = 0.25$

4 Copy and complete

a $\frac{1}{20} = \frac{5}{100} = \square\%$ **b** $\frac{2}{5} = \frac{\square}{100} = \square\%$ **c** $\frac{9}{25} = \frac{\square}{100} = \square\%$

5 Copy and complete

a $\frac{8}{25} = \frac{\square}{100} = 0.\square$ **b** $\frac{18}{200} = \frac{\square}{100} = 0.\square$ **c** $\frac{12}{48} = \frac{\square}{4} = 0.\square$

6 Work out

a $\frac{3}{7} + \frac{3}{7}$ **b** $\frac{4}{5} - \frac{1}{5}$ **c** $\frac{1}{2} + \frac{1}{3}$ **d** $\frac{5}{8} - \frac{1}{4}$

7 Change these percentages into fractions (cancel down where possible).

a 40% **b** 25% **c** 45% **d** 8% **e** 46%

8 Change these fractions into percentages.

a $\frac{7}{100}$ **b** $\frac{8}{25}$ **c** $\frac{1}{2}$ **d** $\frac{3}{5}$ **e** $\frac{32}{200}$

9 Which number is the odd one out? $\left(\frac{1}{4}\right)$ $\left(0.25\right)$ $\left(1.4\right)$

10 Ryan scored $\frac{12}{25}$ in a French test. The pass mark is 45%. Did Ryan pass the test? If so, by how much?

11 Write the following in order of size, smallest first.

a $0.42, \frac{2}{5}, 45\%$ **b** $\frac{1}{20}, 0.2, 10\%$ **c** $\frac{7}{10}, 73\%, 0.68$

118

Work out

1　117 × 27　　　**2**　136 × 64　　　**3**　1353 ÷ 41　　　**4**　364 ÷ 28

5　Biscuits are packed in boxes of 24. How many boxes are needed for 1272 biscuits?

6　461 eggs are packed into 38 boxes of 12 eggs. How many eggs are left over?

7　53 people each pay £32 to watch a cricket match. How much do they pay in total?

8　Copy and complete

　　a □ ÷ 39 = 12　　　**b** 837 ÷ □ = 31　　　**c** □ × 48 = 1536

9　36 Easter eggs are packed into each box. A supermarket orders 17 boxes. How many Easter eggs is this in total?

10　A gardener plants 72 rows of daffodil bulbs. Each row contains 42 bulbs. Eventually all the bulbs are packed into crates. Each crate contains 24 bulbs. How many crates does the gardener fill?

1　Work out
　　a 16 − 7.4　　　**b** 2.19 − 1.8　　　**c** 3 − 0.17　　　**d** 43.6 − 16

2　Which answer is the odd one out?

　　| 7 + 1.2 |　　| 9 − 0.8 |　　| 4 − 2.1 |

3　Jean weighs 59.2 kg at the start of the week. At the end of the week she weighs 58.83 kg. How much weight has she lost?

4　Copy and complete the number chain.

3.86 —+→ 4.4 —=→ □ —−→ 6 —=→ □

5　Copy and complete

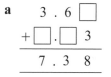

```
a    3 . 6 □
   + □ . □ 3
   ─────────
     7 . 3 8
```

```
b    2 . 9 □
   + 5 . □ 8
   ─────────
     □ . 3 4
```

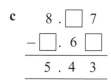

```
c    8 . □ 7
   − □ . 6 □
   ─────────
     5 . 4 3
```

6 Answer true or false.

a $3.18 \times 10 = 318$ b $0.462 \times 100 = 46.2$ c $13.6 \div 10 = 1.36$

d $429 \div 100 = 4.29$ e $23 \div 10 = 0.23$ f $3.8 \times 100 = 380$

7 Five books cost £28. How much does each book cost?

8 Work out

a 6.12×6 b 0.36×4 c $7.8 \div 5$ d $34.4 \div 8$

e 3×2.59 f $30.1 \div 7$ g 8×2.37 h $12.96 \div 6$

9 A rubber weighs 8.6 g. How much do 7 rubbers weigh?

10 Copy and complete the number chain.

| 6 | $\times$ → | 1.48 | = → | | $\div$ → | 3 | = → | |

HWK 6M ———————————————————————— **Main Book page 316**

1 Which is larger?

(20% of £30)   or   ($\frac{1}{3}$ of £21)

2 Increase £80 by 30%.

3 Grace has £60. She spends 35% of this money. How much money has she got left?

4 Which answer is the odd one out?

| $\frac{4}{5}$ of 40 | | $\frac{3}{5}$ of 60 | | 40% of 80 |

5 Work out

a $\frac{5}{6}$ of 24   b $\frac{3}{8}$ of 16   c $\frac{2}{3}$ of 21   d $\frac{9}{10}$ of 80

6 There were 40 people in a swimming pool. One hour later there were 30% more people in the pool. How many people were in the pool at this time?

7 Copy and complete

a $\boxed{}$% of 400 = 40   b $\boxed{}$% of 900 = 180   c $\frac{1}{\boxed{}}$ of 42 = 7

d $\frac{1}{\boxed{}}$ of 18 = 6   e $\frac{2}{3}$ of $\boxed{}$ = 12   f 5% of $\boxed{}$ = 6

You may use a calculator for the remaining questions.

8 16% of the crowd of 41 500 people watching Chelsea play Liverpool are Liverpool fans. How many Liverpool fans were at the match?

9 Which is greater?   (6% of £90)   or   (8% of £68)

What is the difference between the answers?

10 Mark earns £2900 each month. He is given a 3% pay rise. How much does he now earn?

11 Which answer is the odd one out?

$$12\% \text{ of } £4900 \qquad \frac{1}{3} \text{ of } £1773 \qquad \frac{4}{5} \text{ of } £735$$

12 Work out $(69\% \text{ of } £8300) - \left(\frac{3}{7} \text{ of } £10\,801\right)$

HWK 7M ——————————————————————————— **Main Book page 317**

1 Write these ratios in simplified form.
   a $56:72$ **b** $24:30:42$ **c** $0.9:0.4$
   d $40:15:45$ **e** $2\,\text{kg}:500\,\text{g}$ **f** $5\,\text{m}:20\,\text{cm}$

2 £7200 is shared between Carlos and Kavya in the ratio $1:2$. How much money does Kavya get?

3 The floor areas of a living room, dining room and bedroom are in the ratio $8:3:5$. All the rooms are to have the same carpet. If the bedroom carpet costs £600, how much does the living room carpet cost?

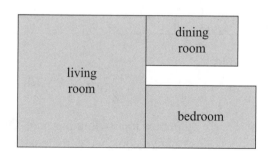

4 A farmer has 30 hens and 20 goats. Another farmer has hens and goats in the same ratio. If the second farmer has 45 hens, how many goats does the second farmer have?

5 The ratio of pound coins to 50p coins in Jack's money box is $7:4$. What fraction of the coins are pound coins?

6 Barnaby wants to make 36 pancakes. He has 280 g plain flour, 6 large eggs and 900 ml milk. Has he got enough ingredients to make 36 pancakes? Explain your answer fully.

12 pancakes
100 g plain flour
2 large eggs
300 ml milk

7 Janice gets $\frac{4}{7}$ of £63 000 from a will. She shares this money between her daughter, son and herself in the ratio $5 : 3 : 10$. How much more money does her daughter get than her son?

8 If 5 kg of potatoes cost £5.50 and 3 kg of carrots cost £4.50, how much do 8 kg of potatoes and 2 kg of carrots cost?

5.4 Rounding numbers

HWK 1M ——————————————————— **Main Book page 323**

1 Round these numbers to one decimal place.

    a 3.82   **b** 7.91   **c** 23.45   **d** 3.718   **e** 8.649

    f 8.0231   **g** 38.693   **h** 24.2684   **i** 4.325   **j** 2.5813

2 Which of these numbers round off to the one decimal place number shown in the middle?

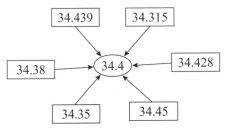

3

    a Write down the length and width in cm, correct to one decimal place.

    b Use a calculator to work out the area of the rectangle, giving your answer to one decimal place.

4 Work out these answers on a calculator and then write them correct to one decimal place.

a 3.2×7.3 b $12 \div 9$ c $9.14 \div 8.7$ d $4.106 + 3.689$

e $0.4 \div 0.092$ f $\sqrt{3.8}$ g $5.3 - 1.938$ h 29.2×13.67

5 Write down any number between 32 and 33 which has been rounded off to one decimal place.

6 Answer true or false.

a $7.837 \rightarrow 7.8$ (to 1 decimal place)   b $6.95 \rightarrow 6.9$ (to 1 decimal place)

c $650 \rightarrow 700$ (to nearest 100)   d $18.16132 \rightarrow 18.2$ (to 1 decimal place)

HWK 2M	Main Book page 324

1 Write the following numbers correct to two decimal places.

a 5.6837   b 24.7168   c 0.49468   d 0.08712

e 104.8652   f 9.0594   g 13.06283   h 427.60843

2 Write down the smallest number that would be rounded up to 8.94 to two decimal places.

3 Work out these answers on a calculator and then write them correct to two decimal places.

a $19 \div 7$ b 5.81×6.93 c $\sqrt{7} \times \sqrt{6}$ d $38 \div \sqrt{67}$

e $\dfrac{1.47}{2.1 + 0.03}$ f 3.14^2 g $\dfrac{5.2 + 1.72}{3 - 0.83}$ h $\dfrac{7.4}{2.18^2}$

4

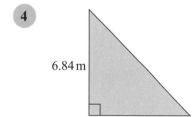

6.84 m

5.29 m

The area of a triangle is $\dfrac{\text{base} \times \text{height}}{2}$

Kevin works out the area of the triangle opposite to two decimal places. Ariana works out the area to one decimal place. Work out the difference between Kevin's and Ariana's answers.

5 Round the following numbers to the degree of accuracy indicated.

a 7.5168 (1 d.p.)   b 16.0917 (1 d.p.)   c 0.07104 (2 d.p.)

d 836.693 (1 d.p.)   e 4.63278 (2 d.p.)   f 47.83348 (2 d.p.)

6 Terri rounds 15.7012 to two decimal places. She writes the answer 15.7 Explain clearly why she is not correct.

7 Use a calculator to work out $\dfrac{3.164 + \sqrt{19}}{5.3^2 - 2.417}$, giving your answer to two decimal places.

$201.6 \times 3.9 \approx 200 \times 4 \approx 800$

Decide, by estimating, which of the three answers for each calculation below is closest to the exact answer.

Calculation	A	B	C
1	19.8×101.2	2000	3000	1000
2	2.03×39.7	100	60	80
3	$405 - 199.83$	150	300	200
4	$3008 \div 201.4$	15	150	60
5	$503 \div 20.3$	250	25	5
6	1.99×61.2	120	60	12
7	1503×9.91	15 000	3000	1000
8	$0.312 + 0.673$	0.1	1	5
9	7.19×16.03	10	200	110
10	19% of £598	£12	£60	£120
11	$\sqrt{63.75}$	6	8	12
12	8.23×5.08	40	13	400

1 A box of chocolates costs £5.95. Estimate the cost of 30 boxes of chocolates.

2 A pen costs £3.05.
  a Estimate the cost of 15 pens.
  b Find the exact cost of 15 pens.

3 Dani earns £793.25 each month. Estimate how much she earns in one year.

4

Estimate the area of this triangle.

9.2 cm

4.05 cm

5 Use estimation to decide which calculation below gives the largest answer.

| 7.03 × 29.6 | | 12.1 × 19.78 | | 1587 ÷ 8.14 |

6 Dean buys 3 pineapples, 2 boxes of washing powder and 5 tins of beans. Estimate the total cost.

pineapple	£1.96
washing powder	£4.05
tin of beans	£0.49

7 The area of a rectangle is 2406.5 cm². If its length is 59.92 cm, estimate its width.

8 Tallulah pays £71.50 each month into a savings plan. She does this for 10 years. Estimate the total amount she pays into the plan.

9 Write down each calculation and insert the correct answer from the list given. Use estimation.

a 3.91 × 6.04 **b** 4076.4 ÷ 79 **c** 29% of 2016

| Answers: | 51.6 | 584.64 | 23.6164 |

5.5 Probability 2

HWK 1M **Main Book page 329**

1

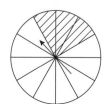

What is the probability of spinning a shaded part on this spinner?

2 | C | H | A | N | C | E |

One of these letters is selected at random. What is the probability of selecting:

a the letter N   **b** the letter C?

3 | 2 | | 3 |

| 5 | | 7 | | 11 |

| 13 | | 17 |

One of these prime numbers is chosen at random. What is the probability of choosing:

a a number less than 6

b a single-digit number

c an even number?

4 There are 18 socks in a drawer. 8 are blue, 7 are grey and the rest are red. Jan selects a sock at random. What is the probability that she selects:

a a grey sock   **b** a red sock   **c** a green sock?

5 Gareth says that if he throws a dice six times, he will definitely get a 6. Is he correct? Give a reason for your answer.

6 One of these cards is selected at random. What is the probability of selecting:

a the letter R

b a ?

c a vowel?

| H | A | R | D | E | R | ? |

7 A fair dice is rolled. Are you more likely to get an odd number or a number greater than 4? *Explain* your answer.

8 | 1 | 3 | 4 | 4 | 7 | 9 | 9 | 9 | 10 | 11 |

A card is selected at random. Find the probability of selecting:

a a number greater than 9   **b** an even number

c a prime number   **d** a square number

9 A bag contains green balls and yellow balls. If one ball is randomly removed, the probability of taking a green ball is $\frac{2}{3}$. If there are 24 balls in the bag to begin with, how many green balls are left in the bag after the first ball is removed, which is green?

126

1 A ball is selected at random from this bag. Find the probability that it is:
  a red   **b** green   **c** white
  d If one red ball is removed and one white ball is added, find the new probability of selecting a green ball from the bag.

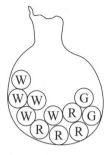

2 One card is picked at random from a pack of 52. Find the probability that it is:
  a the ace of hearts   **b** a king   **c** a red card   **d** a diamond

3 Sally needs to throw a '6' with a fair dice to start a game. What is the probability that she will *not* get a '6' with her next throw?

4 Den has 7 goldfish and 3 pink fish in a tank.
  a He selects a fish at random to give to his nephew. What is the probability that he selects a goldfish?
  b After giving one goldfish to his nephew, he buys four more pink fish. If he now selects one fish at random, which type of fish is he most likely to pick? *Explain* your answer.

5 ⬜ T ⬜ H ⬜ I ⬜ N ⬜ K

These cards are shuffled. One card is selected at random and turns out to be an 'H'. What is the probability that the next selected card is a 'K'?

6 Cards with numbers 1, 2, 3, 4, 5, 6, 7 and 8 are shuffled. The first card chosen is the 4 and the second card chosen is the 6. Find the probability that the next card chosen will be:
  a the 2   **b** an odd number   **c** more than 5

7 There are blue balls and yellow balls in a bag. A ball is removed 25 times and replaced each time. The blue ball is chosen 5 times and the yellow ball is chosen 20 times. If there are 5 balls in the bag, how many balls are likely to be yellow?

8 The table below shows the number of different coloured beads in a bag.

Colour	Number of beads
blue	24
red	4
green	30
pink	25
yellow	7

A bead is chosen at random. Which colour has a probability of $\frac{5}{18}$ of being chosen? Give a reason for your answer.

9 Two coins are thrown.

   a Make a list of all the different things that could happen (e.g. tail head).

   b Find the probability that both coins land on heads.

   c Find the probability that both coins land on tails.

10

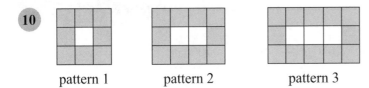

pattern 1   pattern 2   pattern 3

Black and white tiles are used to make the patterns shown above.

   a One tile is selected at random from pattern 4. What is the probability that it is black?

   b One tile is selected at random from pattern 5. What is the probability that it is white?

UNIT 6

6.1 Metric and imperial units

HWK 1M ——————————————————————————— **Main Book page 350**

Remember: 1 km = 1000 m,   1 kg = 1000 g,   1 litre = 1000 ml

1 Copy and complete each statement below.

    a 7 kg =   g   **b** 9 m =   cm   **c** 3.5 m =   cm   **d** 4000 g =   kg

    e 60 mm =   cm   **f** 2.6 km =   m   **g** 7.5 litres =   ml   **h** 200 g =   kg

    i 30 cm =   m   **j** 9.4 km =   m   **k** 8500 g =   kg   **l** 4.6 cm =   mm

    m 8000 ml =   litres   **n** 50 cm =   m   **o** 0.4 kg =   g   **p** 350 m =   km

2 Fiona drank 300 ml of water from a 2 litre bottle. How much water is left in the bottle?

3 Terry has walked 9.2 km in a 10 km race. How many metres has he still got to walk?

4 How many 250 ml drinks can be taken from a 1 litre bottle?

5 80 cm is cut off a 2.5 m piece of wood.
How long is the remaining piece of wood?

6 Gwen says that an average drinks can contains 330 litres of drink. Is she likely to be correct?
Give a reason for your answer.

7 220 g of flour is needed for a cake. A baker has 2.5 kg of flour at the start of the day.
During the day he bakes 9 cakes. How many more cakes can he bake?

8 Write down the amounts below in order of size, starting with the smallest.

     410 g   0.815 kg   32 g   0.4 kg   1350 g   0.04 kg

HWK 2M ──────────────────────────────── **Main Book page 352**

Reminder:	1 foot ≈ 30 cm	1 kg ≈ 2.2 pounds
	8 km ≈ 5 miles	1 gallon ≈ 4.5 litres

1 Copy and complete each statement below.

a 10 kg ≈   pounds   **b** 90 litres ≈   gallons   **c** 30 miles ≈   km

d 6.6 pounds ≈   kg   **e** 6 gallons ≈   litres   **f** 8 feet ≈   cm

g 44 pounds ≈   kg   **h** 32 km ≈   miles   **i** 6 kg ≈   pounds

2 The distance from Bristol to London is about 160 km. How many miles is this?

3 Tania is 5 feet tall. Mary is 1.48 m tall. Who is taller and by how much?

4

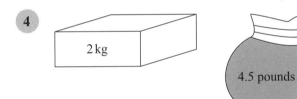

The box and the bag both contain sugar. Which contains the most sugar and by how much?

2 kg

4.5 pounds

5 Jim has 3 gallons of water in a water butt in his garden. How many litres will he have left if he uses 12 litres?

6 Charlie wants 1.1 pound of cheese. In a shop, how many grams of cheese must he ask for?

7

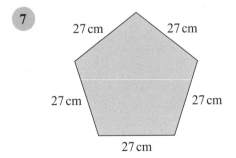

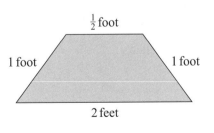

27 cm   27 cm

27 cm   27 cm

27 cm

½ foot

1 foot   1 foot

2 feet

Which shape opposite has the longer perimeter and by how much?

8 Manu wants to buy a cooker which is $3\frac{1}{2}$ feet wide. He wants to put the cooker in his kitchen in a space which is 102 cm wide. Will the cooker fit? Explain your answer fully.

130

For each of the scales, work out the measurement indicated by each of the arrows.

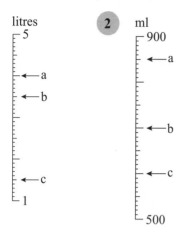

1 litres

2 ml

3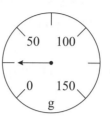

4

5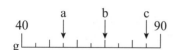

6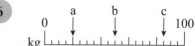

7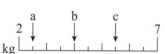

8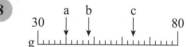

9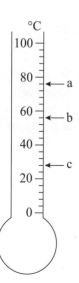

Write down the difference between the arrows:

a a and b

b a and c

c b and c

10

litres

Write down the difference between the arrows:

a a and c

b b and c

c a and b

HWK 4M ─────────────────────────── **Main Book page 355**

1 Find the area of each shape in cm².

a 2 m, 200 cm

b 100 cm, 5.3 m

c 30 cm, 0.4 m

2 Work out

a 6 kg − 400 g (in g)   **b** 0.9 m + 84 cm (in m)   **c** 86 mm + 3.7 cm (in cm)

d 3 km − 784 m (in m)   **e** 5.4 kg − 376 g (in kg)   **f** 8 litres + 360 ml (in ml)

3 A lorry carries 2 tonnes of building material. If 862 kg of material is unloaded, what weight is left on the lorry?

4 John buys bars of chocolate costing 38p, 42p, 35p, 49p and 37p. How much change will he get from a £10 note?

5

3.4 cm

25 mm

4.9 cm

4 cm

2.4 cm

74 mm

Find the perimeter of this shape in mm.

6

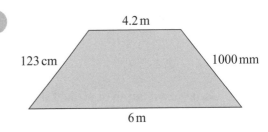

4.2 m

123 cm

1000 mm

6 m

Find the perimeter of this shape in cm.

7 A metal bar weighing 12.35 kg is melted down and made into metal balls, each weighing 130 g. How many metal balls can be made?

6.2 Angles and constructions

HWK 1M ———————————————————————— **Main Book page 358**

Find the angles marked with letters.

1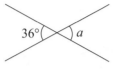

36° a

2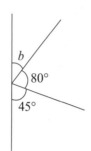

b

80°

45°

3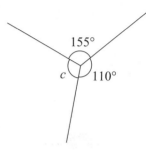

155°

c 110°

4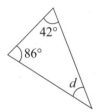

42°

86°

d

5

53° e

60°

6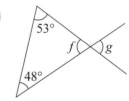

53°

f g

48°

7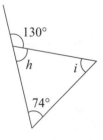

130°

h i

74°

8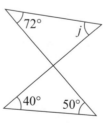

72° j

40° 50°

9 Use a *protractor* to draw the following angles accurately.

   a 75°   **b** 43°   **c** 130°   **d** 115°   **e** 34°   **f** 230°

10 For each angle in question **9**, write down if it is acute, obtuse or reflex.

11

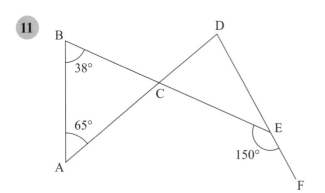

Work out the value of CD̂E, giving full reasons for your answer.

HWK 1E   **Main Book page 360**

Find the angles marked with letters.

1

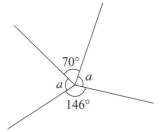

2

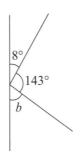

3

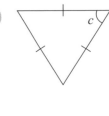

4

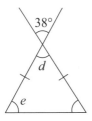

5

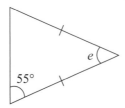

6

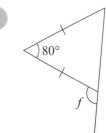

7

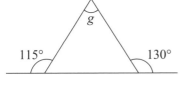

8

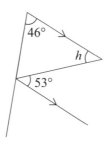

9

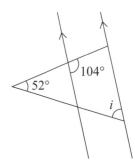

134

10 Two of the angles in a triangle are 75° and 30°.
Explain clearly whether this triangle is isosceles or not.

11 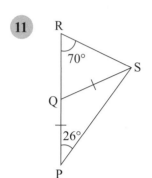 Work out the value of RŜQ,
giving full reasons for your answer.

12 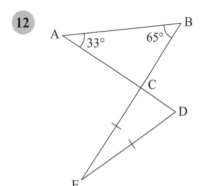 Work out the value of CÊD,
giving full reasons for your answer.

HWK 2M ── **Main Book page 362**

Use a ruler and a pair of compasses to construct the triangles in questions **1** to **3**.
For each triangle, measure the angle *x*.

1 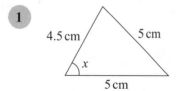   **2** 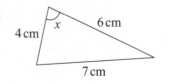   **3**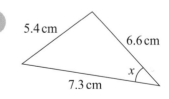

4 Construct triangle PQR where PQ = 7.4 cm, QR = 5.9 cm and PR = 5.2 cm. Measure PR̂Q.

5 Construct triangle ABC where AB = 5.3 cm, BC = 6.4 cm and AC = 6.9 cm. Measure AB̂C.

6 Construct the rhombus below then measure AC.

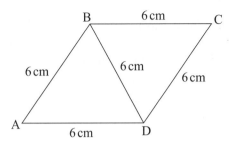

7 Construct the parallelogram below then measure PR.

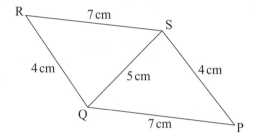

HWK 3M   **Main Book page 363**

1 Draw any 3 straight lines. Use a ruler and compasses to construct the perpendicular bisector of each line.

2

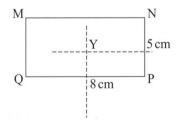

     a Draw this rectangle accurately.

     b Construct the perpendicular bisector of PQ.

     c Construct the perpendicular bisector of NP.

     d Label the point of intersection Y as shown. Measure MY.

3   **a** Construct a triangle DEF with DE = 6 cm, EF = 4 cm and DF = 8 cm.

     b Construct the perpendicular bisector of the line DF and mark the point P where the bisector meets the line DE.

     c Measure DP.

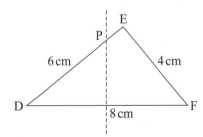

1 Use a protractor to draw an angle of 70°. Use a ruler and compasses to construct the bisector of the angle.
Use a protractor to measure the angles to check that you have drawn the angle bisector accurately.

2 Draw an angle of 80°. Construct the bisector of the angle.

3 Draw an angle of 110°. Construct the bisector of the angle.

4 **a** Construct triangle PQR with PQ = 5.5 cm, QR = 8.2 cm and PR = 6.5 cm.

b Construct the bisector of the angle QP̂R and mark the point Y where the bisector cuts the line QR.

c Measure PY.

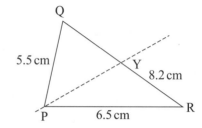

5 **a** Construct the equilateral triangle with each side 6 cm long.

b Construct the bisector of angle BÂC.

c Construct the bisector of angle AĈB.

d Mark the point X where the two bisectors meet. Measure AX.

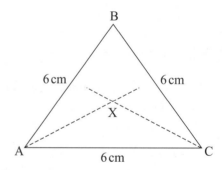

6.3 Three-dimensional objects

1 Name these solids.

a   **b** 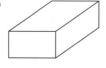   **c** 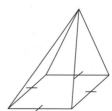   **d**

2 How many faces, vertices and edges has the solid got in question **1** part **c**?

3 Draw a triangular prism. How many vertices does a triangular prism have?

4 How many faces does a cube have?

5 What is the name of this solid?

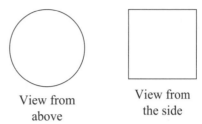

View from above

View from the side

6 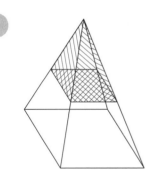 Draw a hexagonal prism.

hexagon

7 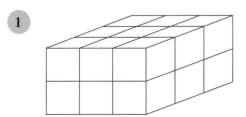 The top of this pyramid (shaded part) is cut off.
Look at the remaining bottom part.
How many faces, vertices and edges does this part have?

8 Draw any solid with 7 faces, 15 edges and 10 vertices.

HWK 2M ──────────────────────────── **Main Book page 373**

1 Draw an accurate net for this cuboid.

138

2 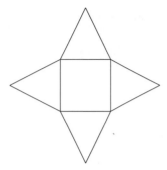 Name the object which can be made from this net.

3 Draw a net for a closed cuboid measuring 4 cm by 2 cm by 1 cm.

4 When the cuboid is made from this net, which face will be directly opposite the ▲?

```
        ┌───┐
        │ 2 │
    ┌───┼───┼───┼───┐
    │ 1 │ ▲ │ 3 │ 4 │
    └───┴───┴───┼───┤
                │ 5 │
                └───┘
```

5 Sketch a possible net for a tetrahedron (triangular pyramid).

6 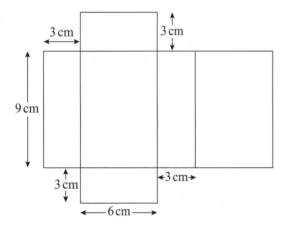 Find the volume of the cuboid made from this net.

7 Draw an accurate net for this triangular prism.

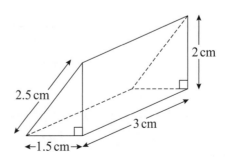

6.4 More equations

HWK 1M **Main Book page 380**

1 Solve these equations:

    a $7n = 35$ **b** $x - 9 = 12$ **c** $4y = 48$

    d $28 + p = 43$ **e** $9m = 72$ **f** $28 - a = 13$

2 Solve

    a $6n + 9 = 51$ **b** $3p - 8 = 1$ **c** $12y - 38 = 82$

    d $6x - 17 = 31$ **e** $5x + 17 = 37$ **f** $7w + 12 = 75$

3 Sarah thinks of a number, multiplies it by 6 and subtracts 18. The answer is 48. Write down an equation then solve it to find Sarah's number.

4 Frances buys 6 pencils and spends 80p on a drink. She spends £2.30 in total. How much did each pencil cost?

5 Solve these equations:

    a $20m - 29 = 51$ **b** $5y + 16 = 116$ **c** $30w - 65 = 145$

    d $8x + 33 = 153$ **e** $6p + 47 = 227$ **f** $15n - 54 = 36$

6

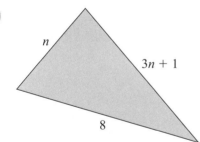

The perimeter of this triangle is 45 cm.

    a Write down an equation involving n then solve it to find the value of n.

    b What is the actual value of the longest side of the triangle?

HWK 2M **Main Book page 381**

1 Copy and fill in the empty boxes:

    a $5n = 3$ **b** $7w = 2$ **c** $1 = 8p$

    $n = \dfrac{3}{\square}$ $w = \dfrac{\square}{7}$ $\dfrac{1}{\square} = p$

2 Solve these equations:

    a $3x + 2 = 3$ **b** $5y + 8 = 10$ **c** $6m - 2 = 3$

    d $4y - 1 = 2$ **e** $10m + 5 = 12$ **f** $9p - 5 = 3$

3 Cho thinks of a fraction, multiplies it by 8 then adds 9. The answer is 12. Write down an equation then solve it to find Cho's fraction.

4 Solve these equations:

a $7n - 3 = 3$ b $10 = 4x + 9$ c $16 + 5p = 20$

d $2 = 8y - 3$ e $14 = 13 + 7w$ f $6 = 15m - 7$

5 Parker solves an equation as follows:

$$5w + 6 = 44$$
$$5w = 50$$
$$w = \frac{50}{5} = 10$$

Explain clearly what mistake Parker has made.

6 Write down an equation for the triangle opposite which involves *n*. Solve the equation to find the value of *n*.

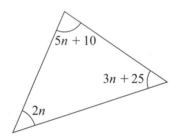

HWK 2E ───────────────────────────── **Main Book page 382**

1 Harrison is asked to solve $3(2n - 5) = 21$

First, he expands the brackets: $6n - 5 = 21$

Now he adds 5 to both sides of the equation: $6n = 26$

Finally he divides both sides of the equation by 6 and cancels: $n = \frac{26}{6} = \frac{13}{3}$

so $n = 4\frac{1}{3}$

Harrison has made one mistake. Explain clearly what this mistake is.

Solve the equations below to find *x*.

2 $2(5x + 3) = 36$ **3** $3(2x - 5) = 15$ **4** $5(2x + 7) = 105$

5 $8(5x - 2) = 144$ **6** $4(5x - 3) = 188$ **7** $12(10x + 1) = 732$

8 $9(4x - 1) = 99$ **9** $10(6x - 5) = 1150$ **10** $20(4x + 3) = 460$

11 $7(3x - 7) = 140$ **12** $2(20x - 9) = 62$ **13** $5(4x + 5) = 185$

14 The area of this rectangle is 38 cm².

2 cm

(3x + 4) cm

a Write down an equation involving x then solve it to find x.

b What is the actual perimeter of this rectangle?

15 Make up any equation which gives the same x value as the equation $6(2x - 7) = 30$.

6.5 Sequences

HWK 1M — **Main Book page 385**

1 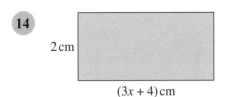 Draw the number of people who would be in the next box.

In questions **2** to **13** copy each sequence and write down the next 2 numbers.

2 19, 16, 13, 10, …

3 400, 200, 100, 50, …

4 4, 5, 7, 10, 14, …

5 4, 2, 0, −2, −4, …

6 2, 6, 18, 54, …

7 1, 3, 6, 10, 15, …

8 3, 6, 12, 24, …

9 0.04, 0.4, 4, 40, …

10 4.1, 3.8, 3.5, 3.2, …

11 256, 64, 16, 4, …

12 3, 8, 15, 24, …

13 5, 15, 45, 135, …

14 A man eats too much. Each month he puts on another 2 kg. If he weighs 82 kg at the end of March, how much will he weigh at the end of June?

15 Each year Maggie gets a £550 pay rise. At the end of 2018 she earns £16 100. How much will she earn at the end of 2022?

16 Write down the sequence and find each missing number.

a | 5 | | 23 | 32 | 41 |

b | 31 | 25 | 19 | | 7 |

c | −13 | −10 | −7 | | −1 |

d | 64 | 32 | | 8 | 4 |

142

In questions **17** to **19** copy each alphabet sequence and write down the next 2 letters.

17   a, c, e, g, …

18   a, b, d, g, …

19   h, k, n, q, …

20   Finally, write down the next term in each of these sequences.
   a 4, 4, 8, 24, 96, …   **b** 0, 5, 12, 21, 32, …

HWK 2M ——————————————————————————— **Main Book page 385**

1   You are given the first term and the rule for several sequences. Write down the first 4 terms of each sequence.

	First term	Rule
a	9	add 3
b	73	subtract 6
c	96	divide by 2
d	5	double

2   Write down the rule for each of these sequences.

a 93, 81, 69, 57   **b** 0.1, 0.5, 0.9, 1.3   **c** 243, 81, 27, 9

d $4\frac{1}{2}, 4, 3\frac{1}{2}, 3, 2\frac{1}{2}$ **e** $-2, -3, -4, -5$ **f** 7, 14, 28, 56, 112

3   Here is a sequence using matches.

     ?

Draw the next picture in the sequence and write down how many matches are used.

4   The rule for the sequences below is '*multiply by 2 and subtract 1*'.
   Copy each sequence and find the missing numbers.

a $3 \rightarrow 5 \rightarrow 9 \rightarrow 17 \rightarrow \square$

b $\square \rightarrow 15 \rightarrow 29 \rightarrow 57$

c $\square \rightarrow 7 \rightarrow \square \rightarrow \square$

5 Write down 5 terms of a sequence with the rule 'subtract 8' where none of the terms is a whole number.

6 Copy this pattern and write down the next three lines. Do not use a calculator!

$1 \times 99 = 99$

$2 \times 99 = 198$

$3 \times 99 = 297$

$4 \times 99 = 396$

7 Every year a population of rabbits trebles and adds 1. There were 10 rabbits at the start of 2010. How many rabbits will there be at the start of 2020?

8 **a** Copy this pattern and write down the next two lines.

$4 \times 8 = 32$

$44 \times 8 = 352$

$444 \times 8 = 3552$

$4444 \times 8 = 35552$

b Copy and complete $444\,444\,444 \times 8 =$

9 Jan has 4 gerbils at the end of July. Each month the number of gerbils trebles but 6 gerbils die. At the end of which month will there be 84 gerbils?

HWK 3M ──────────────────────────────── **Main Book page 387**

1 Here is a sequence of shapes made from sticks.

Shape number n:	1	2	3
Number of sticks s:	5	9	13

a Draw shape number 4 and count the number of sticks.

b Write down the rule for the number of sticks in a shape.

'The number of sticks is ____ times the shape number and then add ____.'

c Write the rule connecting n and s without using words, i.e. write '$s = \ldots\ldots$'

144

2 These dots make a sequence.

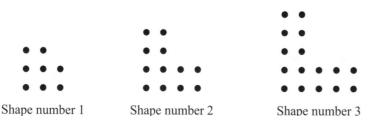

Shape number 1   Shape number 2   Shape number 3

a Draw shape number 4.

b Make a table:

Shape number, n	1	2	3	4
Number of dots, d	8	12	16	

c Write down the rule.
'The number of dots is ____ times the shape number and then add ____.'

d Write the rule connecting n and d without using words, i.e. write '$d = $ ......'

3 Here is another sequence of shapes made from sticks.

          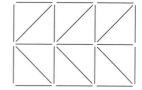

Shape number 1   Shape number 2   Shape number 3

a Draw shape number 4.

b Make a table:

Shape number, n	1	2	3	4
Number of sticks, s				

c Write down the rule.
'The number of sticks is ____ times the shape number and then add ____.'

d Write the rule connecting n and s without using words, i.e. write '$s = $ ......'

4 A sequence of shapes made from sticks has the rule $s = 5n + 1$, where s is the number of sticks and n is the shape number. How many sticks are used in shape number 8?

5 Another sequence of shapes made from sticks has the rule $s = 4n - 3$, where s is the number of sticks and n is the shape number. In which shape number are 25 sticks used?

1 The nth term of a sequence is $3n + 7$. What is the value of:

a the first term ($n = 1$) b the fourth term ($n = 4$)

c the fiftieth term ($n = 50$) d the thousandth term ($n = 1000$)?

2 Write down the first 5 terms of a sequence if the nth term $= 4n - 2$.

3 Which formula below for the nth term gives the sequence 3, 5, 7, 9, ...?

| $3n$ | $4n - 1$ | $2n + 1$ | $n + 2$ |

4 Write down the first 5 terms of a sequence if the nth term $= 6n + 1$.

5 Which formula below for the nth term gives the sequence 7, 11, 15, 19, ...?

| $n + 4$ | $7n$ | $7n + 4$ | $4n + 3$ |

6 Match up each sequence and the correct formula for the nth term from the list given.

a 6, 11, 16, 21, ... b 7, 14, 21, 28, ... c 1, 4, 9, 16, ... d 1, 4, 7, 10, ...

| $7n$ | $3n - 2$ | $n + 5$ | n^2 | $5n + 1$ |

7 Explain clearly whether 46 belongs to the sequence with n^{th} term $= 6n - 2$.

8 A snail is at the bottom of a well which is 30 m deep. Each day the snail crawls up 3 m but each night it drops down 2 m. How many days does it take the snail to reach the top of the well?